D1274781

SIX-LEGGED SCIENCE

NOTES ABOUT END PAPERS

AT FRONT, tracks of walking insect or insects, made by persuading them to walk over smoked glazed paper, and then dipping this in lacquer. Two records are provided; above, adult female *Tenebrio molitor* L., a mealworm beetle, and below, adult male *Blattella germanica* L., the german cockroach. The former shows well the zig-zag progress (the centre line caused by the trailing abdomen of the female, loaded with eggs) and also the fine double parallel lines resulting from the paired claws on each tarsus slipping on the smooth paper. The latter shows better the footprints in close groups of three, formed by the three feet on each side coming down in succession at almost the same place.

AT BACK, wing tip movement of females of several species of horseflies recorded on smoked paper on a rotating drum, separated by time traces. The large jogs one second apart, the small jogs 1/5 second apart. A part of the figure eight path can be seen, in the two left hand series, and frequency can be counted from any trace.

SIX-LEGGED SCIENCE

BRIAN HOCKING
University of Alberta

SCHENKMAN PUBLISHING CO., INC.
Cambridge, Mass.

SCHENKMAN PUBLISHING COMPANY, INC.
CAMBRIDGE, MASSACHUSETTS

Library of Congress Catalog Card Number: 67-29324
Printed in the United States of America

PREFACE

This book is written for people. Could insects read, some of of them might find it interesting, for it is intended to convey to people some of that information about insects which they need to live in harmony with these animals. While written for the general public, it is hoped that these essays will have some special interest for scientists in any field who want a quick glimpse of another. I hope that in particular it will be found useful by biologists whose training has been, as it often is, inadequate in entomology. Entomologists in embryo should find some vitelline material in it; if it appeals to any later instar, larva, pupa, or imago, so much the better.

In the references at the end of the book I have attempted to provide something for everybody, from the naive to the sophisticated, but this has not always been possible. I have also tried to include references to support the more outrageous statements I have made in the text. The primary references for each chapter are the insects themselves, the ultimate court of appeal for all entomological questions, always in session close at hand.

It is a pleasure to thank my colleague Dr. George E. Ball and my wife, both of whom read everything, made many helpful suggestions, and contributed in less direct ways. I would like to record my debt to many other colleagues who have read and commented on parts of the text or helped me with advice on particular points. The work of many scientists shows in these pages. The names of a few appear at the end of the book; I hope others will agree with my view that to attempt complete documentation in a book of this kind would be inappropriate.

Much of this material was originally prepared for radio or television. Responses to it in these forms have encouraged me to recast it for publication. I am indebted to the Canadian Broadcasting Corporation and to CKUA Radio Station, Edmonton, for permission to do so.

I am indebted also to the many authors and publishers whose works I have quoted, and especially to the Society of Authors (p. 71), Doubleday and Company (from: *the coming of archy* p 79, from: *random thoughts by archy* p. 83, and from: *certain maxims of archy* p. 89), Ward, Lock and Company (*I'm Very Fond of Gardening* p. 81), Curtis Brown and J. M. Dent and Sons (*The Termite* p. 81, and pp. 116 and 155), The Spectator (*The Cicadas* p. 84), Random House (*The Fly* pp. 87-88), Sidgwick and Jackson (*Perch-fishing* pp. 89-90), and Michael Flanders (p. 174). For the more imaginative illustrations I am indebted to Miss Gail Hughes, the mundane drawings are my own, as are the unacknowledged verses. A final thank you is due to Miss Diana Rediker of the Schenkman Publishing Company, for her meticulous attention to vital detail in the final manuscript which rendered everything presentable.

Metamerically yours,

BRIAN HOCKING

Edmonton, Canada
September, 1967

CONTENTS

Preface v

INTRODUCTION

1 The Elephant's Scientific Child 3

THE NATURE OF INSECTS

2 Armoured Ancestors 13
3 The Temperature of Sex 25
4 Forerunners in Flight 34

SOME INSECT SENSES

5 Education, Advertising, and Ears 49
6 Six Legs and Twelve Noses 56
7 The Eyes Have It 64

THE VARIETY OF INSECTS

8 Verses to Order 75
9 With Beetling Brows 91
10 Scales, Straws, and Silk 100
11 Bloody Diet 109
12 Lord of the Dunghill 120
13 Gall Enough in Thy Ink 131
14 Bees' Knees and Corsages 138

INSECTS AND US

15 And Two Khaki 149
16 Populations, Pesticides, and Poisoners 158
17 Bombs, Bugs, and the Future 168
18 Centennials and Posterity 175

References 185

Index 193

INTRODUCTION

In which a young elephant demonstrates some features of the scientific method for us, and while doing so, gets into trouble. Six legs would have helped him. His evolution proceeds apace introducing us to similar happenings among the insects.

1

The Elephant's Scientific Child

RUDYARD KIPLING's Just So Story, The Elephant's Child, with its fanciful account of the origin of the elephant's trunk, makes a good illustrative parallel in explaining the way in which the proboscis-like mouthparts of the true bugs developed from what we might call the mere-smear mouthparts of their ancestors, the biting insects. Over the years I have found this parallel less and less useful as a teaching device; apparently fewer and fewer students are familiar with the original stories. This is unfortunate, not only because it means I have to find a new device, but more especially because besides being rattling good tales for children of all ages, the Just So Stories are full of important morals in science. If it's a long time since you read them, go back to them and read them to your scientific children; they will enjoy them, and perhaps I may yet be saved from having to find that new device.

The first moral comes from the Elephant's Child himself with his " 'satiable curtiosity," the most essential characteristic of a scientist, and one which no great scientist has lacked. You may give a man or woman the best training available in the scientific disciplines, saturate him with the writings of the scientific masters, and provide him with free scope and the best equipment, but if he lacks an insatiable curiosity he will produce perhaps perfect, but nonetheless mediocre results. And yet, how many parents and teachers fail to encourage this fearsome spark with which every child is born, and even take active steps to quench it? I say fearsome because it is of course a dangerous thing, as our hero the Elephant's Child learned well. Parents and teachers are inclined to play it safe. The very framework of education, children sitting in rows in a classroom like, as Maria Montessori said, "rows of butterflies transfixed with a pin" is antagonistic to curiosity, even about butterflies. It requires courage to allow a child's curiosity to grow; and judgement.

I may illustrate this point by a personal anecdote which relates to the true beginning of my scientific career, my first deliberate experiment. It happened in this way: my brother and I had collected a pile of the remains of fire-crackers, rockets, and other pyrotechnic items which are probably still to be found lying around the back streets of any suburb of London, England on the morning after Guy Fawkes' night. We were younger than I care to remember. From these remains we extracted with penknife and spoon a formidable pile of greyish powder. We each had an hypothesis concerning this material; I said it would burn and he said it wouldn't, (he tells this story the other way around, his memory being somewhat faulty), but we were both curious. With the courage of his convictions and the prerogative of his extra years he agreed to conduct the experiment, while I acted as an impartial observer. It burnt. Indeed it burnt better than I had hypothesized, costing both of us our eyebrows and causing some consternation in the neighbourhood; but the hypotheses were tested and our curiosity survived. Our parents knew what was afoot but, though it must have cost them some grey hairs, they did not intervene. At the time we probably thought we were getting away with something. We look back with gratitude.

This insatiable curiosity, if it is kept alive, is God's greatest gift to a teacher. In fact teachers only need to teach where curiosity has been stifled; where it has been nurtured they have but to direct learning, and usually find themselves stimulated to learn. Thus develops a proper relationship between student and teacher. Nobody who has stopped learning can hope to teach effectively.

How much easier it is to direct curiosity than to teach in the absence of it. And how much more profitable.

I use the word science here in a somewhat restricted sense: that knowledge which has been arrived at by the scientific method of hypothesis and experiment, and the processes of arriving at it, of extending the bounds of knowledge by scientific research. I am not concerned with all those manifold and ubiquitous applications of new knowledge which so often pass under the name of science, but which are dependent more on native cunning than on curiosity.

the hypotheses were tested

The curiosity of the child and adolescent, directed by teachers who have traveled the road before, serves to push back the bounds of his own knowledge until in places, after sufficient specialization, they approach the boundaries of human knowledge. If his curiosity persists he may then become a scientist, when it must lead him beyond these boundaries where none can show the way. Learning and research then are comparable and complementary processes. Both depend on curiosity and both can fascinate. If you wish to learn well you must go to an establishment active in research. The learning process is shared by human children with the young of many animals; herein lies the attraction of puppies, kittens, and young elephants. In this sense, the best compliment a scientist may receive is the criticism that he has failed to grow up.

Lessons in the conduct of research may also be learned from the Elephant's Child. On the advice of the Kolokolo bird he set off on a journey into unknown country to find the answer to his fine new question: "What does the Crocodile have for dinner?" A research project is very like a journey into unknown country. He returned from his journey with a new nose and much new knowledge, but without the answer to his original question. He only found the crocodile by the accident of stepping on it. This is a very common feature of research undertakings – the finding of something useful quite other than that which was sought. Walpole coined the term serendipity for this; few realize how common it is. It is not generally known, for instance, that the more important discoveries on which the motion picture industry has been built were made during the course of investigations into the locomotion of animals; specifically, into the gaits of the horse in an attempt to settle a bet between Leland Stanford, Governor of California, and Frederick MacCrellish as to whether this animal ever has all four feet off the ground at the same time when it is trotting (it does). I once found a species of scale insect new to science while investigating the effects of DDT on some very old species of mosquito.

After curiosity, imagination, perhaps the next most important quality in a scientist, comes in. A man without it may overlook important facts simply because he is looking for something else. New areas of knowledge nearly always need new tools to chart them. These tools, new equipment and new methods, demand imagination in their development. Yet you will hear people deny the exercise of imagination to a scientist.

Despite the simplicity of the essential features of the scientific method – hypothesis and experiment – one is never in a position before setting sail from the shores of knowledge to have any precise idea of where one is going to end up, or how long the trip will be. Knowing the coastline well, however, one may anticipate how deep will be the water – and how hot! A scientist must often come back with an answer which, from the point of view of his sponsors, is the wrong one. This is one of the fascinations of science, and one of the perils of sponsoring it; an objective scientist can always have the last word with his critics, for he can only bring back what he finds where they have not been. I can recall running grave risk of court martial during wartime, when an expensive experiment I was conducting for the armed forces produced an answer which was both unexpected and unrelated to the hypothesis which had been advanced. Research, then, is a gamble, but the oceans of new knowledge are so vast that given a pilot with a militant curiosity, a vivacious imagination, and a good knowledge of the shore, the cargo brought back may be unexpected, but it is almost certain to be valuable far beyond the cost of the expedition.

Turning specifically to the biological sciences, the Elephant's Child has some basic lessons for us here. The most important of these relates to evolution. While nobody contends that elephants really did get their trunks by having their noses pulled by crocodiles, or whales their throats by having shipwrecked mariners fix rafts across their mouths, nevertheless these tales leave no doubt in the mind of a child that animals have not always been as they are now. This, the fact of evolution, is perhaps all that need be grasped at the age at which a child is first ready to meet this book. Reading these tales at a more mature age, the curious child is prompted to ask: "Well, how did the elephant get its trunk anyway?" Perhaps he asks his biology teacher, but of course he wouldn't, in this day and age, be spanked with a hairy paw. I am sure no good biology teacher will resent this link with the Elephant's Child's great uncle, the Baboon.

You will doubtless recall the remark made by the Elephant's Child as the Crocodile was pulling his nose: "Led go, you're hurtig be," serving to remind us that evolution is a painful process in which only the fittest survive. The Crocodile – mutation if you will – departs, leaving the demonstration of the manifold advantages of the new character conferred by him to another species, the Bi-Coloured-Python-Rock-Snake. In the conclusion of the tale natural selection operates on this advantageous modification. It takes the form of spankings, administered this time by the Elephant's Child with his new trunk to his various animal relatives, and results in all surviving representatives of the species acquiring the new characteristic.

Biologists, with their constant contact with manifestations of evolution, are inclined to forget how many people still either do not know, or do not fully accept, the facts of evolution. It is a continual surprise to a biologist to meet an otherwise educated person who denies the human implications of these simple facts. Many of the current problems of man appear in a new light when he is viewed in correct evolutionary perspective with his ancestral animals.

Our principal interest in this book lies with the insects. Insects came directly into the picture in our just so story when the Elephant's Child, having returned from his journey, "picked up his hairy uncle, the Baboon, by one hairy leg, and hove him into a hornet's nest." I trust none of your children will ever do this to their biology teachers; the results might be less desirable. Perhaps you will also recall that, " 'vantage number one" which the Bi-Coloured-Python-Rock-Snake pointed out to the Elephant's Child was that his new trunk could be used to kill the fly that 'stung' him on the shoulder (pp. 120, 123). Thus it came about that one evolutionary modification, in the elephant, changed the selection pressure on a fly in such a way as to favour the development of a species with the habit of biting elephants elsewhere than within reach of their trunks. We may surmise too that the elongation of the elephant's nose and its resulting application to the hides of other elephants, led to the thickening of these and hence to an elongation of another nose, that of the peculiar louse with which elephants are still afflicted.

Insects serve better than any other group of animals to emphasize the vastness of the oceans of new knowledge which man may hope to explore. Recent estimates place the probable number of insect species in the world today at around five million. Of these man has so far met and named considerably less than a million species. He is meeting and describing them at an average rate of some 10,000 species annually, but we do not yet know quite how rapidly new species are being evolved (p. 23). Of those that are known by name and appearance, probably not one per cent have revealed the secrets of their life histories and habits. And each species for which these facts are known has some interesting or exciting feature. We may still say then, as Aristotle did more than 2000 years ago, "All nature is marvelous."

Let us hope that we will not be outdone in exploratory research by an ancestral elephant with a mere smear nose. How about setting out for a sail on this exhilarating insect-infested ocean of ignorance? There's room for everybody; but it may end up as a swim.

THE NATURE OF INSECTS

In which those distinctive structural features of insects which relate them to some familiar animals and distinguish them from others still more familiar are set forth. Their manner of reproduction, on which their facile adaptability depends, is then described, followed by an account of how they came to fly and how well they can do this.

2

Armoured Ancestors

THERE is a school of thought, fallen into some disrepute in recent years, which derives us aberrant vertebrates by evolution from an arthropod stock. It is not my purpose to argue this point, but simply to use it as my entrée to a discussion of this ubiquitous group of animals; but first let me be sure that you are receptive to my viewpoint.

Do you turn pale at the sight of a spider, or shudder at the mention of a louse? I knew a man who, during the last war, was three times torpedoed without turning a hair, but who would react in these ways to the most harmless of insects. And this horror of the small beasts that creep and leap and fly is common among the meek and the mighty. I think most of my readers have an attitude towards insects as unhealthy for themselves as for their would be victims. Am I not right in suggesting that when an insect runs across the floor you hasten to slay it? That you strike first and ask questions afterwards? I base this statement on, among other things, the battered specimens which entomologists receive and are asked to identify. But it is not only because they are difficult to identify that this attitude is wrong. Clearly it is bad for the insect. In the long run it is equally bad for you. That blot on the sidewalk that was a large caterpillar was about to transform into a butterfly, which even you could admire. That round, red and black beetle is certainly on its way to eat the aphids off your delphiniums; that brown one to lay an egg, the potential consumer of the mosquitoes that might have bitten you next Sunday week.

From time to time entomologists are approached by persons suffering from a condition known as entomophobia, which can best be described as an attitude to insects so unhealthy as to result in nervous disease. The victim suffers from sleeplessness, irritation, and persistently complains of an infestation by crawling insects, which the most thorough and complete examination invariably shows to be imaginary. To the sufferer, these imaginary insects are very real things, but they are much harder to deal with than a real infestation. I have sometimes prescribed a basic course in entomology, but sufferers seem to prefer the complaint to the cure. The cultivation of a proper attitude to insects will certainly prevent this condition.

A knowledge of the activities of an insect throughout its life is necessary if we would control it, should it take to nesting in our

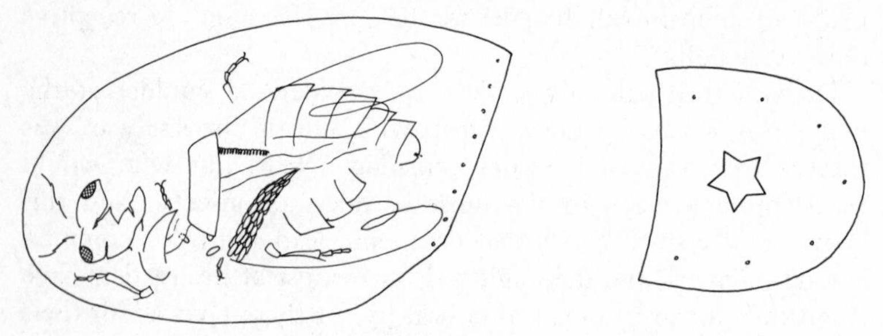

strike first and ask questions afterwards?

underwear or even eating our crops. For many generations this knowledge of the insects was built up, not by the professional entomologist, who is something of an upstart, but by the amateur.

Now people often envisage these amateur entomologists as bearded and bespectacled (p. 177), wielding nets as big as themselves and tearing madly across the fields after their prey, studying insects because they fascinated them. They studied what they pleased and so laid the foundations of our knowledge of insects on a broad basis. Amateur collectors of insects have dwindled in numbers until they are now, like a few of the species they victimized, nearly extinct, and the world of science is poorer without them. As a gesture of appreciation for the work of these men, next time junior brings in a jar of caterpillars or grasshoppers, hide that shudder and restrain the impulse to throw him out on his ear.

Now in any event these myriads of insects, good and bad, are here living with us in the world, and no matter what poisons we may develop against them, rest assured that this always will be so. So many of them are harmful to other insects, and beneficial to human interests, that we should be foolish to wish it otherwise. Let us regard the insects, then, as fascinating fellow occupants of this world, and during our short lives let us learn to profit from their very much shorter ones.

Since we live on land, insects, the terrestrial representatives of the arthropods, are those most familiar to us. For our fishy forefathers, however, this place was taken by the crustaceans. Arthropods include both groups and have been referred to as animals in armour, but since most of them are as small as their lives are short, perhaps we should call them animalculae in armour. The name Arthropoda – jointed feet – reflects this, for joints become conspicuous if you wear your skeleton outside. Last time you ate a lobster you had to get through this armour to get at the meat; compare this with a leg of fried chicken, built on the vertebrate plan like ourselves, with the meat accessible, muscles stretched on the outside of the bony skeleton. Few can recognize kinship with arthropods as they might with dog and bird or even with lizard, frog, and fish; but it may be that all animals are one kindred, and these of the jointed feet have shown such successful versatility that we should respect and perhaps emulate where we may not hope to excel.

A second feature of the arthropods emphasized by their armour is their segmentation or linear repetition. Their bodies are made up of segments like beads on a string, rigid within themselves but movable in relation to those in front and behind. Each bead or segment may carry a pair of legs or other tool-like appendages. This important type of organization in animals is often referred to by biologists as metamerism, meaning 'parts in succession'.

At first sight we vertebrates certainly appear opposed in most respects to arthropods. They are inside out and combine the skin with the skeleton, and they are also in a sense upside down, with the heart above and the nerve cord on the under side. But may it not be that we are the upside down animals, for what criteria

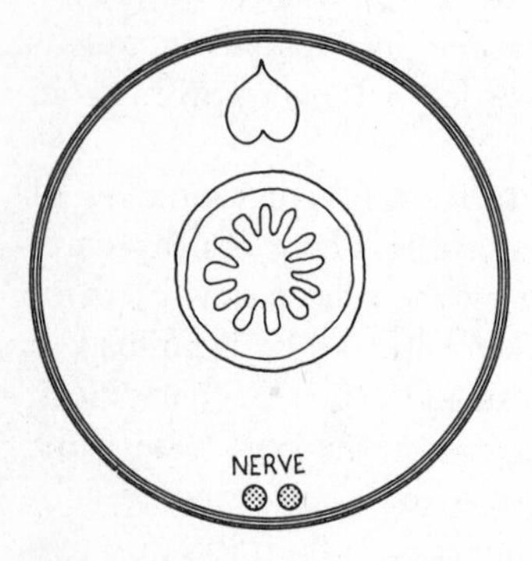

arthropods . . . are inside out . . . and . . . upside down . . .

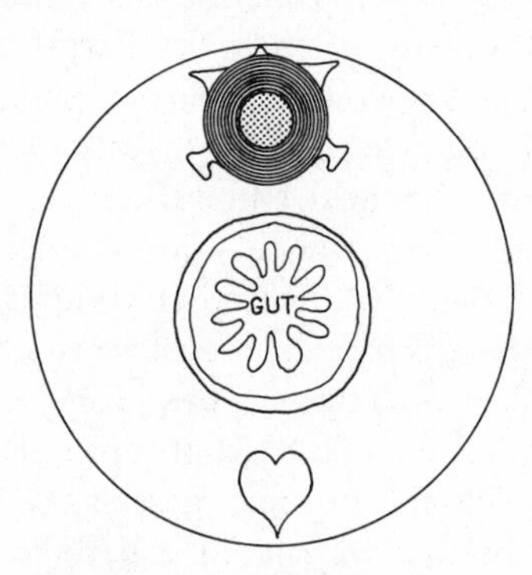

But may it not be that we are the upside down animals?

have we of back and belly but our own? The arthropod nerve cord has autonomous brains in each segment, any one of which can, like an unruly state or province, take over and run things locally without direction from up front. The heart, on the other hand, is just a tube with inlet valves in each segment, pumping blood – if the greenish yellow fluid usually found in it justifies the name – from behind to front, whence it drifts backwards wherever there may be room for it between the organs of the body. Insect blood is disappointing stuff because it contains no haemoglobin and has little or nothing to do with the distribution of oxygen to the tissues. This distribution in most arthropods is done directly through their respiratory systems without chemical intervention. This respiratory system is as complex as the heart and vascular system are simple.

Looking something like portholes in a ship or windows in an aircraft, along either side of the body of an insect are the spiracles, usually two pairs on the thorax and eight on the abdomen. If we could travel, as some parasitic mites do, inside one of the tracheal tunnels which run into the body from these holes, we should be continually required to make decisions – whether to turn left or right – as the tubes fork repeatedly. Each decision would place us in a tunnel about half the area in section of the one we had left, until we would find ourselves in a tube about a thousandth of a millimeter in diameter. This is by no means cramped quarters for oxygen molecules, however, which are here close to their destinations, the cells of the body.

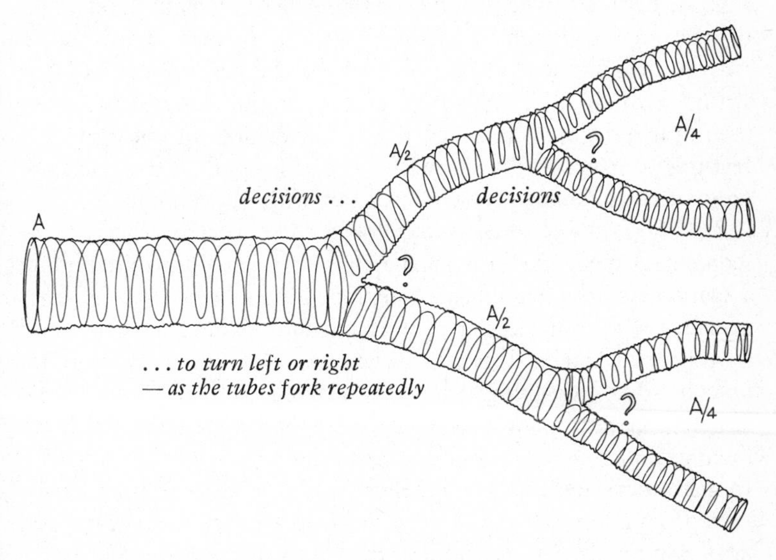

So much for our differences; but now, if you are supple enough, put your left thumbnail behind your back, reach up to the base of your neck, and run it down over the knuckles of your spine.

The regular bump, bump, bump (if you are slim enough) will remind you that you too are a segmented animal, though you have little but your spine left as evidence of this. You too are metameric.

Now that we have a general picture of how arthropods are built we are in a position to appreciate the differences between the classes which go to make up this tremendous phylum of animals. Some of these have long been extinct, but there are four well known classes which are abundant today: the crustaceans, predominantly marine and including our friends the lobsters, shrimps, crabs, and a host of smaller forms; the arachnids, terrestrial, most of them carnivorous and structurally a little peculiar, including spiders, scorpions, mites and ticks; the myriapods, a number of small groups of rather unrelated worm-like animals with many legs, which include the centipedes and millipedes; and the dominant group of all, the insects. The principal way in which these classes differ is in the arrangement of the segments of the body in groups and in the number and nature of their appendages. They are nearly all similar in most of the features we have just discussed for the arthropods as a whole, and most of them seem to have started out with 21 segments.

Taking a closer look at our lobster we see that the first 14 segments have gone into partnership to form one solid region, a combined head and body. The appendages here serve as sense organs, the eyes and feelers; for attack and feeding, the claws and mouthparts; and as legs for swimming or walking on the sea bottom. The remaining segments making the tail have stayed largely separate from each other, and their appendages assist in locomotion, a more exacting activity under water than on land. In many crustaceans these appendages also serve as gills and assist in reproduction. Most crustacea have never left the oceans and have not acquired the breathing tubes of other arthropods.

By contrast we find on examining a spider that it has lost its head, or at least the first two segments of the body. As if in compensation it has an extra pair of legs as compared with an insect, four instead of three. In some arachnids the first of the four pairs does duty as feelers, which have been lost with the second segment to which they belonged. The appendages of segments 3 and 4 serve as mouthparts and, not unnaturally in a group of carnivores, often as offensive weapons, as the fangs of a spider. The extra pair of legs has proved helpful to the spider in walking on its web; anything extra is useful when walking a tightrope.

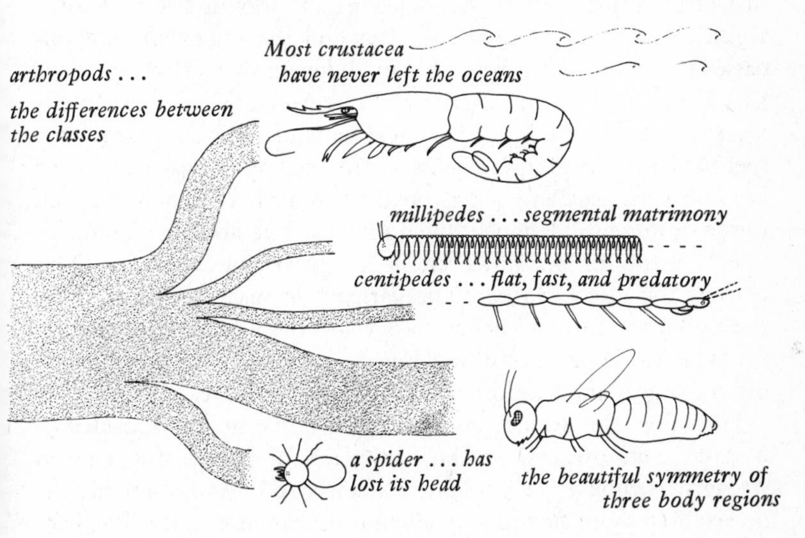

In the centipedes and millipedes, our most familiar myriapods, the first six beads in the string cooperate to form a head, a sensory and feeding region, carrying eyes, antennae, and three pairs of mouthparts. Thereafter the segments are monotonously repetitive. In general each has a pair of very ordinary walking legs – that is, ordinary for arthropods. The centipedes are flat, fast, and predatory and use their first pair of legs to administer poison to their victims. The technical name of the centipedes, Chilopoda, means a thousand feet, the Greek equivalent of the Latin, millipede. Thus they may be said to have a hundred Latin feet, or a thousand Greek feet, but they only have at most 346 actual feet. The millipedes, despite their name, do not have ten times as many legs as the centipedes, but they do appear to have two pairs on each segment. What has really happened here is that the segments have joined up in twos, in a sort of segmental matrimony, while each retains its pair of legs.

The insects (ch. 8) – my special favourites as an entomologist – have the beautiful symmetry of three body regions; a head like that of the myriapods, of six segments; a thorax or trunk of three segments, which carries the six legs and the wings and encompasses the point of balance; and an abdomen of twelve segments, balancing the head and carrying the reproductive organs. In the head and thorax the beads have lost most of their autonomy: the specialized muscle requirements of the feeding equipment on the head and the legs and wings on the thorax have required much fusion and consolidation in these regions. The abdomen compensates for this fusion, however, in its remarkable elasticity. This permits the insects to consume gargantuan meals of many times their own weight, and hence to develop the vast batches of eggs for which they are notorious. But do not call them greedy; it is often many months before they may again indulge.

How does this armour and this upsidedown-ness and insideoutness serve its owners? In the first place, of course, for a given strength a tube is much lighter than a rod. Alone among the invertebrates and first among all animals, the insects fly. But here we must pause to consider the size of insects, which spans roughly the gap between the largest of the protozoa, the single celled animals, and the smallest mammals. A peculiar feature of being this size which monstrous man finds difficult to understand is the possession of much more surface area in relation to one's bulk. The surface area varies only as the square of the length, the bulk varies as the cube, so that the smaller an animal is, the greater, relatively, is its surface. The resistance which the air offers to a body falling through it depends on the surface area of the body, but the force acting on the body, its weight, depends on its bulk. So that the larger a body is the faster it will fall through the air. This is common experience with raindrops – and hailstones! It means in turn, that the smaller an animal is, the more readily it can maintain itself in the air; that pigs might fly is an overstatement, for even many of the largest insects have difficulties.

You have probably heard it said that if your muscles were as-strong for their size as those of a grasshopper you would be able to jump over the Empire State Building. The truth is, you need apologize to no grasshopper for your muscles – they are at least as strong per square inch of section (but see p. 43). It is your weight (forgive me, ladies) which keeps you down. Were we built on the same plan as a grasshopper, but ten times as long, our muscles would be able to exert 100 times the force but our weight would be a thousand times as great. We must be content, therefore, with relatively poorer performance at the high jump and may always need an outside source of power to fly.

The same principle of greater surface area in proportion to bulk or weight affects the function of our armoured animals at every turn, or more specifically at every fork in the tracheal respiratory tunnels which we ventured inside earlier. The two branches of these must each have half the area of their stem, since the gases of respiration move by diffusion which depends on area. Again, since the oxygen required by tissues depends, roughly, on their bulk, this means that diffusion or tracheal respiration is only possible in animals of small size. Indeed, amongst the smallest insects even this respiratory system is superfluous; sufficient oxygen for their tiny bulk can be obtained by diffusion through the relatively vast area of skin.

There are drawbacks to small size too, of course. Evaporation of moisture from the body depends on the surface area, but the amount of moisture available depends on the bulk. So insects are in constant danger of drying up. Here the armour comes into the picture again; its outermost layer is a remarkably efficient moisture barrier. Heat behaves similarly to moisture, and a warm blooded animal the size of the average insect would present tremendous design problems.

Initially, the paired appendages of each segment all served as legs or paddles to move the ancestral arthropod around, but most contemporary arthropods use some of their front legs for putting food into their mouths, as we do. This has become more convenient by a movement of the mouth downwards and backwards, and a swinging of the appendages forwards. More adaptable than we, many have grown their own knives and forks in fantastic cutters and jabbers and claws. This saves dish washing. Others, content with liquid nourishment, have rolled up these appendages lengthwise and combined them in pairs to form plumber's nightmares of pipes which convey secretions – salivary or toxic – outwards, and a variety of fluid nutrients inwards (p. 103).

As yet another weapon in their armoury for life, many arthropods have a remarkable ability to suspend their activities almost entirely for periods of adversity lasting months or even years. In this way they are able to survive conditions of extraordinary severity; temperatures from 60 below zero up to the boiling point, extreme dryness, oxygen lack, and even high concentrations of insecticides (ch. 16).

In the light of all these advantages of the arthropod one is tempted to wonder how man has been able to get a look in at all. But there is – if I may be forgiven the metaphor – one big fly in the arthropod ointment. No external skeleton which can grow in all directions with its occupant has yet been evolved. Even small animals must grow from smaller eggs. The arthropod solution to this problem is time consuming, somewhat clumsy, and hazardous in the extreme; this is moulting. Even the best of arthropods have to go through the ordeal three or four times in their lives, when for some minutes or even hours they are defenceless. Mechanical defence and elaborate protective coloration, eating utensils and spines and stings, even the means to run away, all are laid aside at the time of moulting, for the new armour must necessarily be soft, white, and elastic, unable to withstand even the pull of the animal's own muscles. Here again small size comes, at least in part, to the rescue; places of concealment in which to pass this ordeal are not hard to find in this size range.

Despite concealment, a lot of the heavy mortality which insects suffer takes place at moulting. A lot more is the result of the attacks of other insects, both predators and parasites, and for this man may be ever thankful. The more mortality, the more eggs a species must lay if it is to survive, so that it is hardly surprising that insects need elastic abdomens. Few insects lay less than 100 eggs, and the numbers often run into thousands and occasionally even millions. Laying a hundred eggs means that, if the population is to remain static, there must be 98 per cent mortality before the young reach reproductive age; laying a thousand requires 99.8 per cent mortality. Contrast this with man; in North America today human mortality before the reproductive age is about 5 per cent. The consequences, as we shall see, are far-reaching.

There seems no doubt that the first arthropods evolved in the seas where crustacea, and other groups now extinct, were an immediate success. Perhaps they were too successful and competition in the shallows forced the evolution of species adapted to life in the intertidal and later in the wet terrestrial zones. Somewhere from among this group, about 400 million years ago, appeared the earliest insects. They made a poor beginning with no wings, of small size even for insects, and tied to a moist environment; but from this poor start came three-quarters of our animal species.

It was not until the plants, on which all animal life ultimately depends, developed the mechanical strength to grow upwards that insects learnt to fly (ch. 4). Perhaps they climbed these plants to feed upon them and, when danger threatened, glided from them on flaps projecting from the sides of the thorax. Such flaps are to be seen on early fossil insects; but the flapping of them which resulted in true controlled flight came later. For a hundred million years, no other animal could fly. The air was the insects' and they evolved explosively into it. Their short life cycles and large numbers of eggs favoured rapid evolution. Their small size permitted the development of enormous populations on which natural selection could operate. Small wonder that we now have several times as many species of insects as of all other animals together.

In contrast with the proliferation of insects the vertebrates number only 43,000 species, of which man is but one. He is now so protected from his environment and medicine has so reduced his mortality rate that he is in danger of cutting his own evolutionary throat. Man today adapts so slowly that quite minor changes in the environment – from an insect's point of view – could put him out of business completely. He has, of course, been busily adapting his environment to suit himself, even to the extent of eliminating other animal species. He has had to. The contrast here between us and most arthropods is profound. Our interactions with them are still sufficiently unpredictable that we should watch their progress, and ours in relation to it, with personal interest.

3

The Temperature of Sex

THAT delightful little word s-e-x, sex, gets into the news quite a bit these days: sex in advertising, sex in films, sex in art and literature regardless of its artistic or literary merit, sex in sex education – as if that were something new, sex, in fact, *ad nauseam.* The word sex is usually applied in some rather vague way to copulation, the union of male and female which results in fertilization and reproduction. We shall see that sex is really the converse of this. Since man is so preoccupied with himself, it is usually used in the human context, although it has much more varied and fascinating connotations in plants and other animals.

One of the latest news items on so-called sex to receive wide coverage in the press appeared under the heading "Lovers' hot line." This referred to an instrument christened the snogometer, devised by one Malcolm Picard, a youthful British inventor but obviously with French blood in his veins, to measure the passion – or temperature – of kisses. But I know rather more about sex and reproduction in insects than in people. I have played my part in raising a family of my own, but I have played midwife to myriads of insects, although not usually as an end in itself. I am less likely to fall into error, then, if I write mostly of these more primitive animals, and in doing so perhaps I shall escape some of the vituperation directed at others who have spoken of this rather vital human subject in, of all places, the classroom. Much of what I have to say has implications for man of course, but if

I leave you to infer these, then the criticism will be spread more thinly amongst us.

Reproduction is almost synonymous with creation. It means simply to produce again or to create again; it is rather strange then, that it should so often be regarded as improper in varying degrees, while creation is accorded the highest approval and viewed as a function of divinity. One might perhaps say that reproduction is next to godliness, had this position not been preempted by cleanliness, a dubious virtue usually aimed at inhibiting the reproduction of bacteria.

In the beginning animals reproduced very simply: they divided in two. They grew until they reached the limiting size which their simple organization could maintain and then, in an orderly way, divided themselves into two similar halves. Old age, the limit of growth, meant for them simply reproduction and rejuvenation, to be followed again by growth and old age. Old amoebae never die, they just divide in two. Reproduction in the days before sex,

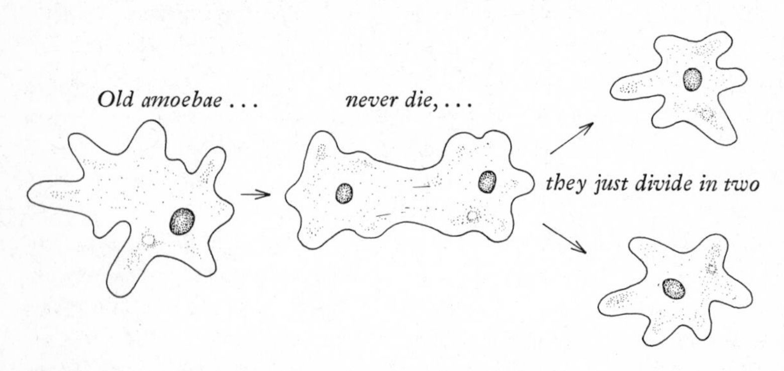

although not so much fun, must have been quite an experience. A later and more efficient variant of this binary fission or dividing in two was multiple fission, a process in which the mature simple animal fragmented into many pieces, each of which grew and reproduced similarly. This was more efficient reproduction because it produced more of the same faster, the aim and object of reproduction. But note that it produced more *of the same;* therein lies the weakness of this sexless reproduction. In this free enterprise world none could compete, for all were cast in the same mould.

Into this best of all possible worlds in which all microbes were equal, the perfect commune, the phenomenon of sex was introduced. How did this happen? According to the Bible it was a cooperative venture between a serpent – the male sex organ – and the eating of the fruit from the tree of knowledge that brought it about. This, of course, begs the question. According to current biological theory too, eating was involved, but eating of a kind usually regarded as somewhat more reprehensible than that of stolen apples, namely cannibalism. It is interesting to note, in both accounts, the connection between eating and sex, between the nutritive and the reproductive appetites.

Many animals will eat each other when overcrowded. When, as with a primitive single-celled animal, eater and eaten are almost identical and neither has a regular mouth, who is to say which has eaten which? Cannibalism at this level is nothing more or less than fusion, the same fusion as that of sex and the very opposite of reproduction. Two animals becoming one instead of one becoming two. Now, however, it is possible when the time comes for this fused animal to reproduce again for the material it contains to be distributed between the two offspring in a manner different from that in which it was distributed between the parents. The offspring may thus differ, both from each other and from their parent and their two grandparents. A much greater variety of individuals is possible as a result of this dual process of combination and separation. Animals which reproduce by this sexual process are more adaptable; some among their number will be suited to survive whatever challenge a changing environment may present. Sex then has, as the biologist puts it, survival value, despite the fact that it cuts down the rate of reproduction. Perhaps this antagonism to reproduction is the drawback to the sexual process, which explains why some organisms without sex are still with us today. Those with sexual reproduction, however, have been much more successful; they have diversified to fit into the environments of the world, the sea, the land, and the air in many more ways. Evolution had a great boost from sex, as the tremendous variety of insects well shows.

So far we have been speaking mostly of simple, single-celled animals. With more complex animals, fusion of the entire organisms presents obvious difficulties, as, for example, those of Hermaphroditus and Salmacis. At this level, groups of the com-

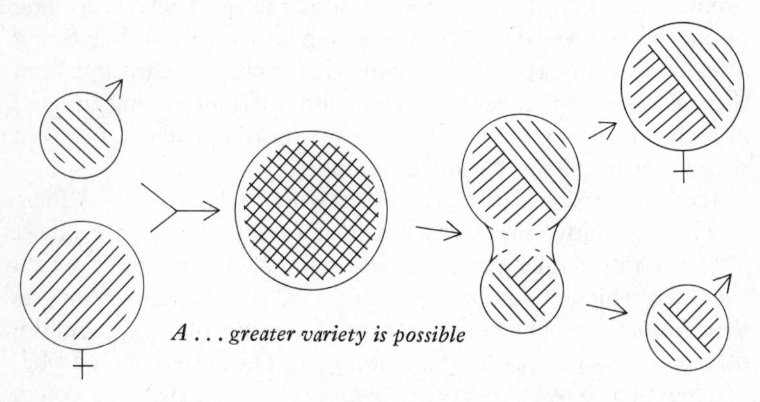

A . . . greater variety is possible

ponent cells of an animal are specialized for particular purposes, and all except those specialized for reproduction, the germ cells, egg and spermatozoon or pollen nucleus, pay the price of specialization; their days are numbered and they die with the individual. Only the successful germ cells retain immortality. And the successful germ cells, of course, are those which meet and fuse with germ cells of the opposite sex. It is of interest to note that even before complex organisms developed, the cells which fused together tended to be of different sizes. That is to say the individuals even of simple single-celled species may be divisible into two groups: large, slow, or effeminate ones and smaller, faster, or masculine ones. This should not surprise us; many a cannibal seeks a victim smaller than herself. This, then, is how sex probably originated, and this is what sex means; the dividing or cutting of a species into two differing halves, male and female. The word comes from the latin *secare*, meaning to cut.

We cannot now go into what decides whether a particular female germ cell will develop after fertilization into a male or a female except to remark that, in general, this is decided by the chromosomes carried by the male cell which fertilizes it. If a human egg is fertilized by a spermatozoon carrying the same kind of sex chromosome as itself, the X chromosome, it will develop into a woman; if it is fertilized by one carrying the other kind, a Y chromosome, it will develop into a man. When the compilers of the book of Genesis had Eve manufactured out of Adam's rib they strangely foreshadowed the discovery of Adam's rib-shaped X chromosome.

With the development of complex animals and the setting aside of a limited number of cells for reproduction, the germ cells, special procedures became necessary for bringing these germ cells from the opposite sexes together – for providing, locally, the overcrowded conditions necessary for cannibalism or, as we should now call it, fertilization. Usually in aquatic animals individuals of each sex associate together and the germ cells are released together or consecutively into the water; then we say that fertilization is external. In terrestrial animals the male usually transfers his germ cells into the body of the female in the process of copulation; fertilization is internal. In either case the process is usually accompanied by some special behaviour which we call courtship and which serves as a sexual selection process not dissimilar to publishing the banns of marriage, ensuring that both partners belong to the same species and are ready for reproduction. But the germ cells themselves have remained aquatic; a major problem of adaptation to the terrestrial habitat has been that of fertilization.

Most higher plants are rather restricted in their movements and are unable to come together either to shed their germ cells or to copulate. This is where the story of the bees and the flowers comes in (ch. 14); most of our familiar flowering plants use insects, often particular kinds of insects, to transfer their germ cells. Flowers, the sexual organs of plants, have come to play an appropriate and highly respectable role in human reproduction in the corsages of courtship and bouquets of weddings, and also, somewhat ironically, in human death in funeral wreaths. It is strange that the equivalent organs of animals have the greatest difficulty in earning even a vestige of respectability.

With this background, let us now take a somewhat closer look at sex and reproduction specifically among the insects. Most insects are bisexual and oviparous, with internal fertilization; that is their processes differ from our own principally in that they lay eggs instead of giving birth to living young. But the insects are such a tremendously diverse group of animals that examples of almost every type of sexual peculiarity and reproductive procedure can be found amongst them.

One of the most widespread peculiarities is parthenogenesis, or reproduction without fertilization. This crops up unexpectedly in many kinds of insects and often makes an unholy mess of an experiment. The ovum is possessed of such zest for life that it is impatient not only of fertilization, but also often of an eggshell, and the young are usually born alive. In the plant lice this is the normal procedure during the summer months, when males may be unknown and females give birth to living young in such numbers that a single female breeding unchecked for a single season could, it is said, cover the land surface of the globe a half a mile deep with her offspring. This serves to emphasize what I was saying earlier about the antagonism between sex and reproduction. But when a hardy egg is needed in the fall to survive a hard winter, *it* is a fertilized egg.

This brings us back to the question of temperature. Now although I have said sex is basically determined by the chromosomes, its development may be affected by a number of outside factors, among which temperature seems to be one of the most important. Recently several entomologists have shown that some of our mosquitoes are particularly susceptible to the influence of temperature. All that is necessary to change a male mosquito into a female mosquito is to catch him young enough and keep him warm. This may be of some practical interest since male mosquitoes do not suck blood (ch. 11). What starts out as a male larva winds up as a female adult. The change from maleness to femaleness is not sudden, but gradual, depending on the temperature. A continuously graded series of adult mosquitoes from fully male to fully female in all of the sex characteristics, external and internal, can be obtained by rearing them at increasingly high temperatures. Indeed, other things being equal it is possible to tell the temperature these mosquitoes were raised at by estimating their degree of femaleness. Similar but less striking effects have been noted in some other insects.

Most of us find it peculiar, if not repulsive, that the females of many predatory insects and spiders often eat their male partners during or after mating with them. But what we feel about it is irrelevant; this has important biological meaning. In the first place, while the process of mating is controlled by the locally autonomous brain in the genital segments, this brain may be overruled by the central or federal brain in the head. The head of the male is usually the nearest part of him to the jaws of the female; this naturally is where she starts eating, and all his federal restraints are thereby removed. This is so effective that when mating is a problem in the laboratory culture of insects, as it often is, beheading the partners is usually worth trying. But there is more to it than this. When the male has transferred sperm to the female, unless there are many more females than males he is of no further value to the species except as an item of diet. And who could be more worthy of this male meal than the female who must ripen her eggs and raise his young? Could this be an atavistic echo of the origin of sex itself in single-celled animals? It certainly has survival value. And yet in some of the dance flies the male seems to take out insurance against this happy fate, presenting the female with some other edible insect he has captured before attempting to mate with her. Lest this should not delay her long enough, he wraps it up in a balloon or in silk spun from special glands. Perhaps the sex ratio is abnormal in these flies. The ultimate in deception is found in still other species in which the female is presented with an empty ball of silk: men were deceivers ever.

It has been well known for many years that in the honeybee fertilized eggs will develop into fertile females or queens if appropriately well fed, but into sterile females or workers otherwise. Unfertilized eggs, however, develop into males known as drones. This serves to reduce variation within the colony and hence to make for social unity, while ensuring variation between colonies. It appeared, then, that the control of sex in the offspring rested on control of fertilization by the queen. But it has recently been discovered that fertilized eggs may also develop into males; when they do, the workers eat such male larvae before they mature, recognizing them because they develop in worker cells. Bees, it should be noted, are reared at an almost constant temperature in the hive. It would be interesting to know how temperature differences would affect these developments.

There are insects, too, in which a single individual may function successively as male and female, and there is also a variety of sexual mosaics in which the right side may be male and the left female. Mosaics or gynandromorphs are bizarre beasts indeed if the male should be blue and the female red, or one smooth and the other hairy. Perhaps the most incredible procedure of all is that found in some parasitic wasps in which the cells of the embryo, when they number a thousand or two, suddenly become autonomous, each resumes the function of an egg, and each proceeds without further fertilization to develop into a separate embryo on its own. In this way many thousand animals can be produced from a single egg, a possibility which can only be realized by a parasite surrounded by abundant and appropriate food. The offspring, naturally, are all genetically identical, and especially are all of the same sex. Human sexual deviates appear normal beside what we may find within a single insect species.

These varied, fascinating findings raise all kinds of questions regarding the ways in which chromosomes exert their influence, and they suggest procedures and instruments which might prove fruitful in studying these topics, so close to the heart of biology. That of the snogometer is unlikely to be among them, but the temperature of sex is clearly of more than passing interest.

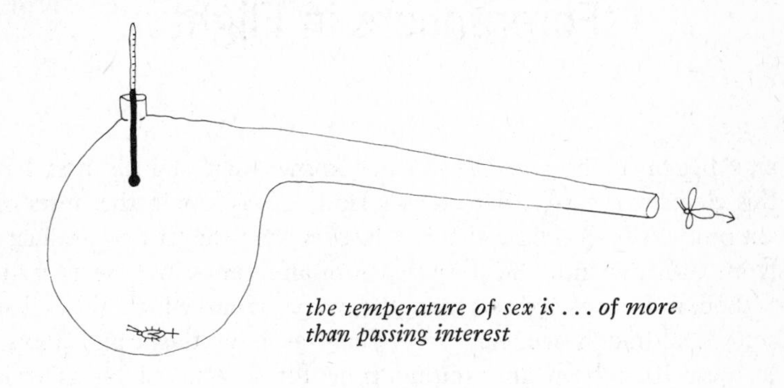

the temperature of sex is . . . of more than passing interest

4

Forerunners in Flight

LIFE began in the sea. We do not know what animals first left this element for the drier, denser land; this is lost in the mists of antiquity. We do know that the insects were the first to graduate from the land into the least dense of life zones, the air (nearly a thousand times lighter than the water from which they first came), although we can only guess at how this came about. It must have been an exciting time for insects, much as it is for us today on the verge of space.

The first insects had no wings, and the early plants on which most of them fed had no upright stems or trunks and branches but grew prostrate over the ground. As life became more abundant, competition for sunlight forced the plants to grow upwards into the air carrying with them their leaves and the insects which fed on them. This was three hundred million years ago; and then rather suddenly, it happened. Perhaps, having exhausted the food supply of the plant they were on, they jumped voluntarily and glided from the top of one plant to the base of another. Perhaps they were pushed or driven from their high perches by predatory enemies, for by this time insects were around that preferred to get their vegetable food second hand. Perhaps, as Russian workers have recently suggested, they were blown from the plants, for the world was a windy place in those days; windbreaks were only just coming into being.

Never at a loss, this thrusting into a new environment proved an opportunity to the insects rather than a hazard. They were well prepared for it; their light, tubular skeletons, quick reactions, small size, and tremendous reproductive powers ensured the rapid evolution of many forms increasingly able to take care of themselves in the air. At first they just glided ever greater distances on ever larger flap-like projections from the sides of the body. The best gliders reached new food and escaped their enemies and survived. Then something, perhaps just the rush of passing air, started these flaps vibrating like the reed in a wind instrument, a clarinet or accordion. The hum of wings is a musical sound, that is it has a definite pitch; this is characteristic of the species and sometimes of the sex. It may even have been the vibrating wings of insects and the music they made that first gave man the idea for this variety of musical instrument. In any event, an instrument in which the reed consists of the front wing of one of our common grasshoppers can be persuaded to yield a tuneful reminder of this possibility. The early wing flaps had no muscles to maintain their vibrations; eventually some of the muscles of the legs, released from the constant chore of moving these, joined forces with others from the body wall to power the wings.

Once the air was conquered, the insects were largely able to escape competition except from their own kind. For a hundred million years they had the air to themselves and made good use of it. This is at least a part of the reason why today we have more species of insects than of all other animals together.

It could not last forever of course; several early groups of reptiles, larger and heavier than the insects, next succeeded in following them into this exciting new environment, tempted there maybe by the abundant insects as food. With their greater size they needed enormous wing surfaces to maintain themselves in the air. This seems to have overtaxed their powers, for shortly the reptiles encountered the dual adversity of nudity and falling temperatures, together with competition from their upstart offspring, the birds, and their flying forms became extinct. The birds had a new advantage: warm blood gave them a more efficient, flexible power plant. And they had evolved feathers, which though nothing but tattered and exaggerated reptilian scales, combined excellent mechanical and aerodynamic properties with adaptability for insulation, thus cooperating with the warm blood so to speak.

The mammals, the last animals to become airborne a mere 30 million years ago, used a different approach. The wing of a bat like that of an insect is built of skin, but mammal skin is soft and bony support had to be provided. This came from the fantastic fingers of the front limb; a sort of ultimate glorification of the humble webbed foot of frog or duck. Finally, as it were yesterday, short-fingered man, inspired by his precursors in the air, built himself wings, and drives them through the air with fuel distilled by nature from countless organisms of the past.

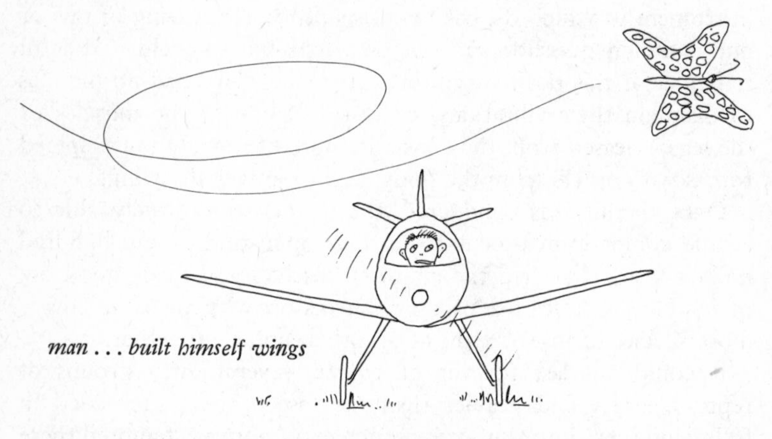

man . . . built himself wings

Flying fish and a few other animals have been partially successful in the air, but the true fliers of today are limited to the insects, with perhaps five million species; the birds with several thousand; the bats a few hundred; and from the primates to the single species, man; with outside help.

Insect fliers started out with two pairs of wings, but most of them now either have one of these pairs modified for some other purpose – protective wing covers in the beetles, balancing organs in the flies – or else have the two pairs coupled together to function as if they were one. Very small insects hardly need wings at all to keep them airborne; many have narrow strip-like wings with fringes of long hairs, especially on the trailing edges. On this small scale a fringe of hairs compares well with a continuous flap for effectiveness, and wears much better. Among larger insects, wings with a tattered fringe are usually a sign of old age. The paddle-shaped legs of insect swimmers are commonly augmented by a marginal fringe of hair, and there is even one group of small parasitic insects which, paralleling the penguins, flaps its fringed wings under water to propel itself in search of its aquatic hosts. The larger an insect is, the bigger its wings in proportion to the body, and most long distance fliers like locusts and butterflies have very large wings which flap rather slowly. A high frequency of wing flapping is usually found in smaller insects which can maneuver well, like the housefly.

It is at first difficult to understand how the apparent up and down flapping of flat plates sticking out from the sides of the body of a fly achieve their end. Note first, however, that the leading edge of an insect's wing is more strongly stiffened by veins than the trailing edge; this combined with the manner of articulation means that the trailing edge is deflected by air pressure away from the direction in which the wing is moving. So a wing on the right side going down behaves like the blade of a propeller of right-hand pitch, but when coming up the pitch is reversed to left-hand. This effect is further enhanced by the fact that the actual path traversed by the wing tip is an elongate, curved, inclined figure of eight, with its lower end displaced forwards and its upper end backwards. This was first demonstrated a century ago by the ingenious French experimenter Marey, who affixed a fragment of gold leaf to the wing tip of a tethered insect and shone a light on it so that he could see the path it traced. He went further, and by the simple expedient of introducing the tip of a smoked glass fibre into a loop of the trajectory of a beating wing and then examining it to see which side of it was cleaned, he showed that the wings moved downwards in front on the upper loop and behind on the lower. All of this has since been confirmed by high speed cine-photography, and much of it you can see for yourself if you observe carefully, against the light, a large hover fly hovering over a flower. You will probably also notice that the angle the wings move through is not just a restricted up and down one, but may be a full half-circle or more. It is said that the difference between the hum of a hive bee coming in to sting and one in passage of peaceful intent is due to an increase in amplitude of movement of the wings, so that they strike together above and perhaps also below the body. Nobody seems to have stayed around long enough to verify this.

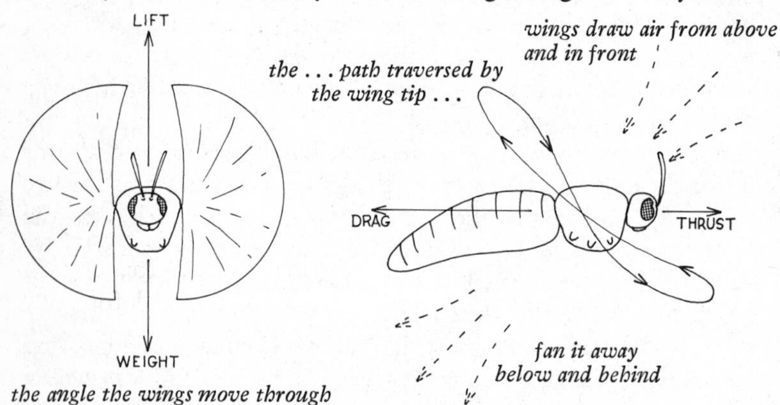

In these complex movements a fly's wings draw air from above and in front of the insect, to fan it away below and behind, and so they generate both forward thrust and lift. They thus function more in the manner of the rotor of a helicopter than of the wings or propellers of conventional aircraft. To give a more precise aeronautical simile, a fly operates like a helicopter with two single-bladed, semi-rotary, reversible pitch rotors.

The muscles which operate insect wings, with a few exceptions, are not attached directly to them but move them through a complicated system of levers set at their bases in the elastic wall of the thorax. Some idea of the power which is needed to maintain a large insect in flight is obtained from the fact that the muscles, which lie within this box, may comprise a third of the weight of the insect itself. They are very peculiar muscles too; in some of the smaller flies the wings beat, and hence the muscles contract, as many as a thousand times per second. The time required for a complete contraction and relaxation of any ordinary muscle is about a tenth of a second.

But this has little to do with how fast insects can fly. Some forty years back when the world speed record for aircraft was around 200 miles an hour a statement appeared in print, under the name of an American entomologist who should have known better, to the effect that a deer fly could travel at eight hundred and twenty. This caused quite a stir, both the New York Times and the Illustrated London News gave the matter considerable space. Man seemed affronted. The author expanded his views indicating that a "daylight day" circuit of the earth was possible. The basis for this statement was the rather unscientific observation that this insect went so fast that one couldn't see it – or almost. Yet the figure was accepted for twelve years, until a physicist calculated that to drive an object the size of this fly at 800 miles an hour would consume fuel so fast that the whole weight of the fly would burn up in about half a second. He calculated, too, that if such an insect were to collide with a man it would "penetrate deeply"; the force might knock him over.

At the other end of the scale and at about the same time, after prolonged experimentation, measurement, and calculation on many insects, a French worker came to the conclusion that current conventional aerodynamic theory had to be set aside in considering the flight of a bumble bee. He had misconstrued the nature of the wing movements and had not allowed for the elasticity of the thoracic framework whereby the kinetic energy of the wings is carried over from stroke to stroke. This finding has been repeatedly subjected to the tempting misinterpretation, by men with more imagination than French, that a bumble bee ought not to be able to fly at all. Bumble bees fly on unperturbed. Indeed they are among the world's most imperturbable fliers, performing with superb purpose in marginal weather eight degrees from the north pole.

There are plenty of remarkable things about insect flight, but speed is not one of them; in continuous flight 25 miles per hour is about the most an insect can hope for. But the speed of an animal tends to increase with increasing size; some birds can average 60 miles per hour for considerable distances and perhaps a hundred miles per hour for a short distance or in a dive. The abilities of bats are intermediate.

There is much closer equality in the range of flight of which animals are capable; both birds and insects can cover six or seven hundred air miles without rest or food and bats may do nearly as well. The distances which insects can fly without feeding bear directly on their geographical distribution and hence on their evolution. Flight range is of practical importance in connection with disease transmission and insect control; clearly no insect can regularly transmit a disease or a parasite unless it can fly as far as the average distance between one host and the next. If we are to have freedom from mosquitoes in a particular town, we must control their breeding within an area the radius of which is related to their flight range. A common procedure for measuring the flight range of an insect has been to mark a large number of specimens with a coloured dye or radio-active material, release them in a given spot, and then see how far away from this spot they can subsequently be found. This is an expensive and cumbersome method when the flight range is greater than a very few miles. It yields a minimum estimate.

The flight range of an insect, however, like that of an aeroplane, depends only on the amount of fuel which it can carry, the power which is required to support it in the air and to overcome the wind resistance or aerodynamic drag, and the efficiency with which it can use its fuel for this purpose. These three quantities can all be measured for any insect, and an estimate can then be made of the distance which such an insect can fly without feeding or "refueling." This yields a maximum estimate, which must be increased for a tail wind or reduced for a head wind.

The fuel used by nearly all insects in flight is either the nectar of flowers or body fat built up and stored from whatever food the insect takes. The nectar secreted by flowers is a solution of sugars of various kinds up to a maximum concentration of about 75 per cent. Its value as a source of energy is about one-third of that of an equal weight of gasoline, and many flowers secrete as much in a day as the average insect can carry, so that we may look upon flowers as insect filling stations. Most nectar feeding insects have a special storing pouch for the fluid which they will fill to capacity if they are caged with a generous supply. The pouch can then be exposed by dissection and its contents measured by withdrawing them with a small syringe. The capacity is variable and best expressed in terms of the empty weight of the insect: some of our mosquitoes can carry a load of nectar equivalent to about 50 per cent of their empty weight; the honey bee can carry about 75 per cent, some blackflies up to 125 per cent; that is to say they may weigh 2¼ times as much after a meal as before it.

Locusts and some butterflies and beetles use body fat as the fuel for flight. Weight for weight this will give about three times as much energy as the strongest nectars, that is to say about the same as gasoline. This is a great asset for long range flight, but full advantage can't be taken of it because the insect needs water too; the nectar-fliers combine this water with their fuel. In spite of this, the insects which have the greatest flight range are, in general, those which utilize fat as fuel.

How much power does a flying insect need? This question can be answered best if it is divided into two parts: first, how much power does it need simply to maintain itself in the air, as in hovering flight; secondly, how much power is needed to push it forwards through the air? The power which an insect needs to support itself depends on two things, its weight and the amount of air which the wings are fanning downwards in a given time. The former is easily measured; the latter may be estimated from a knowledge of the wing area and wing length and the frequency and amplitude of wing movement. The results show that the power required increases more rapidly than the weight. Very small insects require very little power in proportion to their weight to keep them in the air. The same general principle holds for birds, bats, and other animals, and this is one reason why man himself never learnt to fly until an auxiliary source of power became available to him.

The power required to propel an insect forwards through the air can be measured by means of a wind tunnel and an aerodynamic balance similar to those used in aeronautical work. The drag or wind resistance varies with the transverse sectional area of the insect and the square of the speed. This means that the power varies as the cube of the speed; that is, to double the speed of flight, this part of the power output must be increased eight times. At low cruising speeds of flight about the same amount of power is required to propel an insect through the air as is required to support it in the air.

How efficiently can the insect provide this power? In using nectar or fat as fuels for flight, some of the energy which they contain is lost in the digestive system and muscles of the insect. There are further losses in the form of friction in the wing articulations and eddy losses, or turbulence, in the slipstream produced by the beating wings. The ratio of the actual work which can be done in flight to the energy contained in the fuel consumed is the overall efficiency of the system. Losses in the digestive system probably amount to about 5 per cent. The maximum efficiency of human muscle is about 25 per cent. The action of insect wings resembles, as we have seen, that of an aircraft propeller, which has a maximum efficiency of about 85 per cent. The combined effect of these losses, then, means that less than one fifth of the energy supplied can finally be used in flight.

Values of this overall efficiency obtained experimentally are still lower. The insect is attached to the tip of a light, balanced arm by means of a strip of aluminum foil sealed on to its back with wax. When it flies, the arm rotates and the speed and distance which it moves are recorded electrically. On this apparatus the insect flies until it can fly no more – in terms of aeroplanes, until the gas tank is empty – and then it is fed a measured amount of a sugar solution from a micro-syringe. Within a matter of seconds the insect is again ready to fly. It is again allowed to continue until it can fly no more, and the distance and speed are recorded. The work done can be calculated and divided by the energy in the meal that was given the insect to compute its efficiency. The highest continuous efficiency for any insect is only about 5 per cent. The reason, however, is not far to seek. If the flight muscles of these insects are weighed, it is found that the power output per unit of weight is often several times as high as the highest values recorded for human muscle, and the efficiency of muscle is known to fall off quite rapidly as the power increases. This maximum efficiency of about 5 per cent is obtained when the insect is flying at its normal cruising speed; at higher speeds the efficiency is less still, until at the maximum speed of flight it is very low indeed. This is natural, since the power required at higher speeds increases so rapidly. This does not alter the fact that the *forces* exerted by insect muscles are comparable, proportionately, to those exerted by our own (p. 21).

Knowing the fuel capacity, the power required, and the efficiency, calculated speeds and ranges of flight agree well with the best estimates from observations in the field mentioned earlier. The highest speed was 14.7 m.p.h. for a large horsefly, the highest for the honey bee was 9.4. The highest cruising or continuous speed recorded was only 8.4 m.p.h. for the same horsefly; the honey bee cruised at speeds up to 8 m.p.h.; mosquitoes at speeds up to 3.7. The flight range of four species of mosquito varied from 13 to 33 miles. Horseflies ranged up to 63 miles, a common species of blackfly 72 miles, and the honey bee 28 miles. We might add here that although nectar has only one third the energy value of gasoline, one gallon of it is good for some 6 million bee-miles. The maximum endurance in flight can also be calculated, and since this affects the distance which insects may be carried by the wind, it is also of interest. Values extend from 7 hours for one species of mosquito, up to 35 hours for a blackfly.

The knowledge obtained by these studies on a dozen species can also be used to estimate the range and speed of any other species if there is sufficient information on its dimensions, fuel capacity, and flight habits. Two species which have a reputation for long range flights, a locust and the monarch butterfly, gave flight ranges of 217 miles and 650 miles respectively. The monarch butterfly is so well adapted to long range flying that it seems unlikely that any insect can improve on this range.

By weighing the flight muscles of the insects studied it was found that, although the rate of metabolism per unit weight of the flight muscles of some of these insects was up to 40 times the maximum rate recorded for human muscle, the power output was never more than about 6 times the maximum for human muscle, the difference being due to the much lower efficiency at these higher rates of working. Thus while the flight muscles of the honey bee may have a power output of about $1/17$ h.p. per lb., the maximum for human muscle is only about $1/100$ h.p. per lb. Now the bigger the flight muscles of insects, the more power the insect has for flight. On the other hand, the wind resistance or drag depends on the sectional area of the thorax which houses these flight muscles, so that any increase in the flight muscles also means an increase in the resistance to be overcome. For various reasons, the larger insects have the advantage as far as speed is concerned, and probably the fastest fliers are to be found among the large dragonflies. The maximum speed of a large Australian dragonfly which is reputed to be one of the world's fastest insects comes out at 36 m.p.h. and its cruising speed at 24 m.p.h. These are, of course, air speeds; with a tail wind a higher ground speed could be achieved, and in a dive the air speed could also be higher.

On shakier grounds we may estimate that the maximum speed of the great fossil dragonfly *Meganeura monyi* with its 29 inch wing span was 43 m.p.h., or frighteningly higher in a dive.

As for breaking the sound barrier, insects do this only when they take a ride on a jet plane. It has often been suggested that in the design of aircraft man could learn much from insects and birds. This may be true, but in the matter of speed and efficiency, the aeroplane is already far ahead of the insect; it is likely to be in questions of stability and maneuverability that lessons may be learnt from these six-legged fliers. These figures for speed and range may sound a little silly alongside the performance of modern aircraft, but there is another aspect of the question – how many aircraft can land on the ceiling, dive into the sea and continue as submarines, or negotiate power lines and telephone wires in total darkness? Yet these are commonplace activities of the housefly, the gannet, and most any bat.

SOME INSECT SENSES

In which we pass from some further consideration of structure to essay a journey into the consciousness of insects, to hear with their ears, smell with their noses, and see through their eyes.

5

Education, Advertising, and Ears

"FOR there is no conception in man's mind," wrote Thomas Hobbes 300 years ago, "which hath not at first been begotten upon the organs of sense." Our senses, then, are the basis of what we know, in short, the basis of education. The same goes for insects and for animals generally. But it is wrong to suppose that man knows more than other animals because he has more or better senses. Indeed it is wrong to suppose that he has more or better senses; there is no human sense which cannot be outclassed by some other animal. The eye of the eagle can see eight points where our own can see but one; that of the dragonfly may scan a full 360°, twice our limit of 180°. Bats and many insects can hear several octaves above the range of our ears, a butterfly can respond to the sweetness of a sugar solution two hundred times weaker than we can taste, and a dog can distinguish the scent trails of identical twins long after they have passed.

Man knows more than other animals because he is better equipped to store the information which his sense organs give him and, in lesser degree, because he can supplement his sense organs with microscopes, telescopes, and cameras, and with microphones, radio waves, and tape recorders. Thoughts are of knowledge made. And if Descartes is to be believed, they are also the essence of existence: "*cogito ergo sum;*" and the ability to think depends upon a storehouse of knowledge, provided in turn by the sense organs.

And so we see what close and important ties we have between our sense organs, our education, and our existence. It is a pedagogical axiom that many sensory channels will convey information into the brain better than few. Things seen and heard are learned twice as well as things only seen. This effect is called reinforcement; in our commercial world multiple entry might be a more appropriate term. There are practical limits to this, however; the senses of smell and taste may be of value in the study of chemistry and biology but hardly in mathematics or French irregular verbs, even to those who consider that these subjects stink. Our eyes and our ears, then, are the highroads of our knowledge, our thinking, and our existence.

When I first landed in the New World, many years ago now, I was greeted by a large sign overlooking the St. Lawrence River which said: "Drink Canada Dry;" my immediate thought was, what a hospitable country I had come to! A moment's reflective delving into my long disused knowledge of the geography of the country reminded me of the Great Lakes and the myriads of lesser lakes, and I decided that this was just some cruel New World joke. It was some hours later that the true meaning of these three words occurred to me when I spied the label on a bottle broken in obsolescence by the roadside. Then I realized I had been introduced to the juggernaut of New World advertising; a monstrous juggernaut indeed, dwarfing the educational bicycle and intimidating the teacher who pedals it.

And so there is a traffic jam on the highroads of knowledge; education and the truth competing for space with advertising and the half-truth, or less. When my generation was at school, advertising pedalled a bicycle, sat on the shoulders of a sandwich man, or travelled by horse and buggy. The teacher could compete; but what of the teachers of our children and our children's children?

Radio stations come on the air before many of us are awake and explain to the early risers, who know better, how superior this soap or that toothpaste is to all other kinds. The words are reinforced by music. Outside on the streets billboards and neon signs repeat the lies in monstrous magnification. Then television takes both highroads, eyes and ears, reinforcing the raving of the radio with the image of the billboard. But television may be interrupted by telephone: "Madam, can I interest you in . . . . ?" We hang up, but the damage is done. The newspaper and maybe a magazine arrive; the small proportion of fact or honest fiction is broken up by hurdles of advertising; but perhaps there is a flier where the stream of falsehoods is unruffled by intrusion of fact or story.

Young children are impressionable and almost indestructible; they still seem to grow up and even to learn something. Perhaps amid the tumult and the shouting, the spectacles and the shows, the voice of the teacher may get through, ". . . two and two make four . . . ." Perhaps amid the avalanche of advertising vehicles, amid the longer, lower cars with more headroom and more horsepower, there may be room for skillful teachers to pedal their bicycles of education, exercising truth amid the dollops of delusion. A peashooter may succeed where big guns fail. But do we have to take the chance?

Nature too, of course, is full of both advertisers and educators; the success of the flowering plants depends largely on their enterprise in this field. The flower, containing the sexual organs of the plant, advertises the nectar it has to offer to a visiting insect by its color, form, and scent. This is a nice example of reinforcement. The insect pays for what it gets by transferring pollen from the male organs of one flower to the female organs of another. Other examples are to be found in the warning coloration of poisonous or distasteful plants and animals; the black and yellow stripes of the wasp which say to all who can read this visual language: "Keep off my tail, it carries a sting;" the orange and black of the monarch butterfly: "Don't eat me, I taste simply horrible . . ."

Audible advertising, too, is well represented in nature. The tree-top commercials of bird song, most often a warning to trespassers in the establishment of territory by the male, are a familiar accompaniment of spring. In the chirping of grasshoppers and crickets and cicadas we find again a courtship function (ch. 8). The male repeats for the benefit of any female within range, usually with monotonous regularity: "Here I am, here I am." His statement, as a rule, conveys the additional information, "I am one of your kind," or perhaps it is only intelligible to the female of the same kind. The sound of the male confused tree cricket might be expressed as: pre-ee-ep pip . . . pre-ee-ep pip . . . pre-ee-ep pip, and its human equivalent is, of course, the wolf whistle.

Most of this is honest advertising; part could even be called education. But I might as well admit that among the insects we also have examples of dishonest advertising; flies which carry the yellow and black stripes of the wasp have no stings in their tails; they exploit the sting carried by the wasp. The viceroy butterfly, reputedly palatable, carries the colors of the distasteful monarch, and the cicadas especially can rival any ventriloquist in the projection of their voices, saying, in effect, "Here I am" – when they're not. So perhaps we can blame our dishonest advertising on our ancestry, although this does seem rather a long way back to carry it. Education might have taught us better by now.

The ears of insects may be found on various parts of the body and match, in their range of sensitivity, the range of sounds which insects produce. They differ widely in sensitivity from our ears, and also from our range of voice. This is a situation which provides much opportunity for misunderstanding and deception. Most of the sounds produced by animals, including those which we extort from musical instruments, arise from the vibration of membranes or plates or stretched fibres. The sounds may be supplemented by the resonance of adjacent air filled tubes or chambers. All such things vibrate with a frequency determined by their composition and their dimensions, in such a manner that the smaller they are the higher the frequency or note which they emit. Most insects are so much smaller than we are that most of the noises they make are, inevitably, beyond our hearing range altogether. What we do hear amounts to no more than the bottom notes of the largest insects, often largely accidentally produced. Yet many a poet has been inspired by this: what might he not produce could he but hear the whole song?

The noises insects make are of two kinds, accidental, such as buzzing in flight and rustling and clicking as they walk; and deliberate, produced mostly by organs modified for this purpose. Accidental sounds may serve many purposes, deliberate ones usually serve to bring the sexes together and are of three kinds corresponding to the strings, the percussion, and the brass and wood-wind of our own orchestras. Repetitive though they be, these deliberate sounds have a lot to tell us; a single song may contain many frequencies, some produced by amplitude modulation. The songs of insects include frequencies up to at least 100,000 cycles per second, about three octaves beyond the limit of our hearing. As Sir John Lubbock put it fifty years ago: "The familiar world which surrounds us may be a totally different place for other animals. To them it may be full of music that we cannot hear, of color which we cannot see, of sensations which we cannot conceive. . ."

In the limited understanding we have of insect talk most of it is apparently honest, but there are exceptions: the death's head hawk-moth is one of the very few animals which can invade the interior of a beehive and survive to tell of it. It produces, by miniature wood-wind through the mouthparts, a piping sound which mimics that produced by the queen bee herself using a similar method in the breathing tubes of the thorax; it is thereby enabled to rob honey unmolested.

Stranger than the sounds they make are the ears that insects hear them with. Three kinds cover three separate but overlapping frequency ranges. Hairs which are sensitive to touch and deflection, from whatever cause, interpret to the insect sound waves of frequencies from nearly zero up to about the top notes of a piano, with an optimum about two octaves above middle C. Most insects have these. Organs at the base of the antennae, named Johnston's organs in honour of their discoverer, are well developed in rather fewer insects. These are sensitive to the deflection of the antennae and in some half understood way to

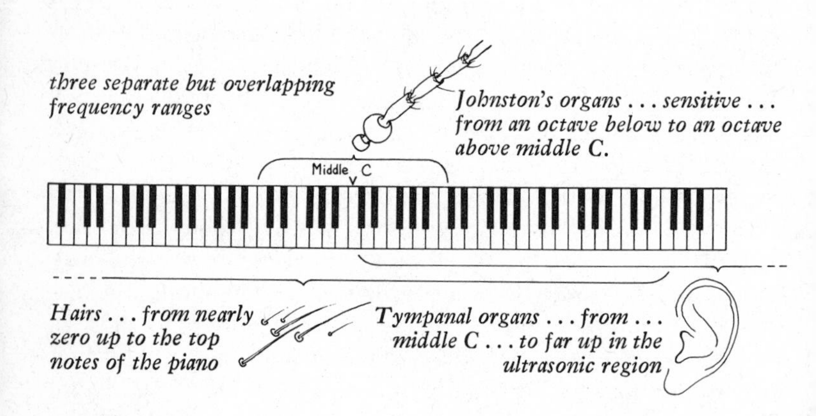

sounds from an octave below to an octave above middle C. Tympanal organs, structurally closest to our own ears, are found in relatively few insects, chiefly those that make deliberate noises. They are sensitive from about middle C to far up in the ultrasonic region. Presumably an insect knows which kind of ear it is hearing with and we may suppose that each ear has its own significance; yet with all this, few insects have what we should call a musical ear, and those that do, usually only in a very narrow range (p. 97).

Both in the natural world then, and in the rather unnatural segment of this which we have carved out for ourselves, we have a full spectrum of communication from dishonesty to truth, with advertising crowding the lower half of the scale and education striving for the top notes of truth. It is well established that the lower the level of education the more effective is advertising. The reverse is also true. Yet one finds, too, the infiltration of advertising, mostly of a rather general kind, into education. There is much in our school curricula directed towards making our children into bigger consumers, instead of more discriminating ones. If education can achieve this latter objective, if it can teach our children of all ages to discriminate, it can remove the chassis from under the advertising juggernaut and thus leave room on the highroads of knowledge for chariots of education, for teachers to ride in state.

The fifteen billion dollars spent annually on advertising in North America, persuading the more gullible of us to buy what we don't want, would go a long way towards educating us to know our real needs. Such a transfer of funds might force the advertisers to cooperate in education by embracing the truth, to the immediate and lasting benefit of us all, of the world and what we produce in it. In this way alone, I think, we may be able to halt the avalanche of planned obsolescences, the armies of hidden persuaders, the myriads of waste makers in our midst, our own worst enemies, before they have carted off all of our natural resources, our wild-life, plants and animals amongst them, by the shortest route to the scrap heap. The last to go undoubtedly would be those which, to date, we have tried hardest to get rid of: those other advertisers and teachers with the peculiar ears, the insects.

6

Six Legs and Twelve Noses

IT may be that, as the song says: "It's dabbling in the dew that makes the milkmaids fair," or it used to be, but it was quite certainly sitting on the old-time three-legged stool that made them stable. This is not to suggest that modern milkmaids are any less fair or any less stable than their forebears, but simply to remind you in these modern times when most floors are flat and most cows milked by machine, of the inherent stability of anything with three legs – table, stool, or even milkmaid. But it is my purpose now to discuss the legs of insects, not milkmaids.

Those who know nothing else about insects are usually well aware that they have six legs, but neither they nor many experts can tell you why. A geometrician might put it this way: any three points are coplanar; so that it matters not how irregular the surface or how variable the length of a leg, a milking stool with three legs never rocks. We may say that a milking stool has three legs because a cow has four – one to spare to kick with, an eventuality which puts a premium on the stability of the stool. An arithmetician will tell you that twice three are six, and in these simple mathematical statements lies the answer to the question: "Why does an insect have six legs?."

We may regard the run of the mill insect as having, in its hexapod undercarriage – for I should remind you that most insects fly and that their legs are retractable – a pair of three-legged stools. Now insects do not, of course, have quite the problem envisaged for centipedes by Mrs. Craster, in deciding which leg to move after which. But their problem may be a sizable one all the same; a horse, with only four legs is capable of 164 different gaits, but nobody seems to have discovered how many more the extra pair of legs adds to this for insects. Of the gaits available to an insect, that most often observed is a surprisingly simple one. The front and back legs on one side are moved at the same time as the middle leg on the other, three legs moving at a time. These are each put down as close to the one ahead of it as possible, except of course the leading leg which must break new ground. This results in a remarkable economy of footprints, each one being used in succession by the three legs on its side of the

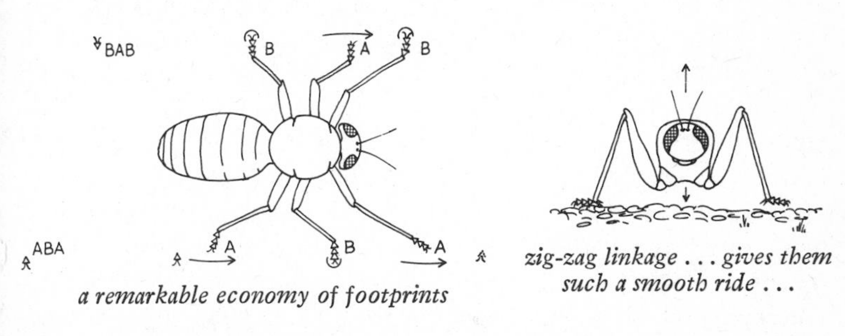

a remarkable economy of footprints

zig-zag linkage . . . gives them such a smooth ride . . .

body. It also results in a characteristic zig-zag progress, which you must have seen when a ground beetle crosses the sidewalk or a cockroach the kitchen floor, for there is alternately more movement taking place on the left side and on the right side.

This very simple gait has one big advantage; any three points are coplanar, that is to say, no problem of nervous coordination is raised, for no matter how irregular the going, the feet on the ends of the three moving legs will all, automatically, be able to make contact with the ground. We may say that, in effect, an insect carries with it two three-legged stools, sitting on each one alternately while moving the other one forward. This is such an obviously sensible arrangement that one is tempted to ask, not: "Why does an insect have six legs?" but: "How does an animal with any number other than six – milkmaid, mouse, or millipede – manage to compete?"

There is another advantage to having six legs, and that is the ability to spare one or two for special purposes other than walking: for take-off or swimming; for hanging on when hitch-hiking, mating, laying eggs, or moulting; for spinning webs, building nests, or even raking up supplies of food. Just as the middle child in a family of three is the most difficult, so the middle pair of legs has the greatest difficulty in serving any other purpose than walking. The middle legs are usually closest to the insect's center of gravity, and hence most deeply engrossed in the problems of locomotion.

The front legs of insects most often have as their additional responsibility some function in connection with eating, a natural result of their proximity to the mouth. Those of the praying mantids are used to catch their prey, those of the dance flies to wrap it up in a silken web, those of the dragonflies to hold it, with some help from other legs, while it is being eaten. If the male climbs on the back of the female to mate, his front legs may have special attachments that serve to hang onto her, as the suction cups, for example, of some water beetles. A few butterflies which spend much of their time airborne and feed only on the nectar of flowers have apparently found front legs to be superfluous, for they are reduced to mere stumps. Their caterpillars, with a more business-like existence, naturally have six good legs and true.

But the hind legs of insects are the most diverse of all. They are close enough to the center of gravity that they can serve special functions in getting the insect around, as the take-off legs of grasshoppers and the swimming legs of water beetles and other aquatic insects. They are close enough to the genitalia that they may assist in mating. Or they may serve to position the eggs when these are laid, as by our more sophisticated mosquitoes, in a neat raft of chevrons afloat on a still pool. Surprisingly, they may also play a part in feeding where this is a social function, as in the bees. The hind legs of bees are provided with rakes, combs, and baskets used with some help from the other legs and from the adhesiveness of honey to assemble compact pellets of pollen to feed the young. And here, for once, the middle legs have a special function. They carry the closest thing in nature to a can-opener, which is used to prise these pellets loose into the cells of the honeycomb.

On being asked how long a man's legs should be Abraham Lincoln is reputed to have replied "... long enough to reach from his body to the ground." This may be all right for a man, but it certainly isn't good enough for an insect, at least when it is adult. Adult insects nearly all have much longer legs than this. Insects' legs are attached low on the side of the body and the first piece points downwards; they then change their minds and with the help of a small wedge-shaped piece, turn the corner, whence a longer piece reaches outwards and upwards, often above the back of the insect. Then downwards again to the ground, for which another change of direction and the longest shaft of all are needed. Apparatus for adhering to ceilings, leaves, webs or water, sticks and stones is carried on the end of this longest shaft. It is this zig-zag linkage which, in cooperation with the two groups of three, gives them such a smooth ride over any kind of country. Some day the salesmen for new cars will get onto this and laud the hexapodan ride of their super-thunderbugs or hyper-fireflies.

We must refer to one other attribute of the legs of insects before passing on to noses, and that is their sensory functions. Many insects taste with their legs, many hear with them, probably all feel with them, and some tell the temperature with them; but only very few, so far as I know, can smell with them. And since most animals have characteristic scents, though these may not be detectable by man, who is a poor smeller, it is not surprising that most animals have organs with which they can detect these scents. Indeed, smell seems to be a more basic and primitive sense than vision. Many animals recognize their own kind and the opposite sex by smell, many find and recognize food by smell; some, like the ants, find their way around by a sort of smell map. The six regular legs, however, are not nosey, they have enough to do.

What do insects smell with? Most importantly with a pair of appendages sticking out in front of the head. I hesitate to give these a name; the layman calls them feelers, which they often are, though this is rarely their most important function. The scientist calls them antennae, and the modern implications of this word in radar and radio make it a less happy choice, although its original meaning – a yard-arm of a sail – does something to redeem it, since most flying insects use their antennae as wind sensors. Perhaps one should coin a word which would cover these three functions plus that of hearing (p. 54), General Purpose Sense Organ Appendages or GEPSOAS. But for the moment let us call them antennae, and remind ourselves that they originated in a comparable manner to the legs. Réaumur, as long ago as 1734, came to the conclusion that the antennae served either the sense of smell "or some other sense unknown to us."

Before we get any deeper into smell, we should draw a line between this sense and its near relative, taste. Mostly we smell things as vapours and taste them as solutions, but this does not apply to aquatic animals. Taste is a very simple sense, detecting saltness, sourness, sweetness, and bitterness; that is all. The flavour of fine food is a synthesis of these sensations superimposed on smell, a much more versatile sense, and a much more acute one. Most people can distinguish between many hundreds of different smells, and where one may need a billion molecules of a substance in order to smell it, many thousands of times this number are needed for tasting.

Now the nature of a nose affects its function, which is of course to sample the air for odours. Our own noses are placed in association with our respiratory systems and, as it were, parasitize the lungs for their samples. We sniff when we would smell better. The antennae of insects are so far removed from their puny respiratory systems, which could hardly contribute more than a microsniff anyhow, that they can get little help from this source and have to go out and get their own samples. Antennae do this by waving around, and when you see an insect waving its antennae, it is a sure sign that there is something in the wind. The effectiveness of antennae for this purpose is increased by plate-like extensions in dung beetles and comb-like extensions in male moths, or by brushes of hair. When an insect is in flight, the forward movement and the fanning of the wings provide a very generous sample.

For a smell organ to work it must receive a certain number of molecules of a stimulating chemical, and this puts the insects at a serious disadvantage in comparison with man on account of their small size; a man can sample air at least a thousand times as fast as can an insect on the ground. Despite this, measurements show that insects smell most things about as well as man does, and experience suggests that they smell some very much better; the ability of some male moths to detect the sex attractant of a female a mile or more away is a case in point. These astounding performances depend on a male awareness of wind direction, as well as on smell. At rest on ground or tree his antennal wind sensors give him this; on the wing he depends on his eyes, that can look forward and back at the same time (ch. 7). So long as he perceives the female scent he flies up-wind, but as soon as he loses it he searches. Thus he homes on his mate, flying up-wind along a cone of odour.

There is a synthetic ingredient of rose oil which the honeybee, despite its smaller sample, can respond to in half the molecular concentration needed for man to detect it. The *Drosophila* fruit flies, the darlings of the geneticist, can detect the smell of alcohol and esters associated with fermentation processes much better than excise men. Time was when these professional busybodies were trained in the recognition of fruit flies and used them as nosey go-betweens in detecting illicit stills. The fruit flies have laid their eggs on ripe fruit since long before excise men were thought of. Indeed, they convey the spores of yeasts, which result in fermentation, from fruit to fruit, and in this way they facilitated the invention of wine and are responsible for the very existence of both vintners and excise men. Wine drinkers would do well to sponsor a female *Drosophila* for the throne of Bacchus; the dew she loves is potent stuff.

homes on his mate . . . upwind along a cone of odour

It is interesting to observe that the insect nose can recognize a smell when it is presented in a mixture with other smells much better than the human nose. This may be connected with the fact that at least six separate parts of each antenna commonly carry olfactory organs. Or perhaps with the existence of two other pairs of organs on the head, the palps alongside the mouth, and three more pairs of appendages at the tail end, all of which may show chemical sensitivity. Whichever way you look at it, twelve noses are in fact microsniffing their way to food or drink, to a mate or an egg-laying site.

In insects, even more than in larger animals, the major senses of smell and vision vary widely in their development, but usually in an inverse relationship to each other. The mayflies and dragon-flies with their enormous eyes, have insignificant antennae; the dung beetles with great fan-like antennae have small eyes. One may guess that the other ten noses show similar reciprocal development but nobody has yet examined this closely. It may be that the limited brain lacks the capacity to process the streams of information which would be provided by two major groups of sense organs. In larger animals both the capacity for a brain and the capacity of it are greater.

While one cannot quite agree with Chesterton's Quoodle, who said:

They haven't got no noses,
The fallen sons of Eve;
Even the smell of roses
Is not what they supposes;
But more than mind discloses
And more than men believe.

nevertheless, in comparison with insects man is poorly off for a nose. Woman however is worse off; both in insects and ourselves, the male smells best – excuse me, ladies – the male has the more sensitive nose.

7

The Eyes Have It

IT is not for nothing that I sound like my eye; that the first person singular personal pronoun sounds, in English and some other languages, very much like the organ of vision; for the eyes often express more fully the personality of their owner than he does himself when he opens his mouth to speak of "I." This expression of personality communicates itself through the eye of the beholder, the fenestration of the soul. Let us suppose now that you look a grasshopper square in the eye. Does its personality come across? What do you see there by way of a soul? Probably nothing unless you have been brought up with grasshoppers; but I would remind you that the inner beauties of your own personality are probably lost, too, on the grasshopper. Eyes so different as those of Kate and katydid need training to appreciate each other. To the perceptive human eye, that of a grasshopper is a slow-motion kaleidoscope, full of depths of colour, reflection, and changes. Meaningless to man it may be, but we should be rash to suppose that madam grasshopper is unmoved.

Sexual selection in the choice of a mate is not the primary function of an eye, but it is an important one. The eyes contribute much to sex appeal; the eyes, to use a euphemism of yesteryear, have IT. The dilation of a girl's pupil that we call a "glad eye" inspires and is in turn inspired by the ballad which a boy writes to her. The saying that "men never make passes at girls who wear glasses" may be true if the glasses have reducing lenses which counteract dilation. What of the insects? The striking differences between the eyes of the male and the female in many groups of insects suggest that the sexual significance may be stronger here. A female horsefly would be dull indeed if unmoved by the diagonal stripes in green and purple, shimmering in the eyes of the male, whose head is literally "all my eye."

Profoundly different from the eyes that read this page, the eyes of an insect are nonetheless the only sense organs it has that can be recognized for what they are by the untutored observer. Its other sense organs are still more different from ours. Let us peer first of all at the structural differences and then see what changes these impose upon the business of seeing. We may find photographic analogies useful here.

The minimum size of a visual sensory element is determined by the wavelength of the light to which it is sensitive. This is similar for all animals. The performance of an eye is determined by the number of such visual elements it contains, that is to say by its size. The sizes of animals themselves are fixed by many different considerations, but are rarely greater than they need to be. Thus, the smaller an animal is, the more of it, proportionally, must be devoted to eyes if it is to see as well as its competitors. Insects are small animals. They see as well as many of their enemies, but they see differently.

Insects' eyes then, are big; the sensitive area in a dragonfly is comparable to that in a mouse, though its head is a fraction of the size. This apparent paradox is explained when we observe that this area is concave in a mouse but convex in a dragonfly. It is nearly 2000 years since Pliny asked in his *Historiae Naturalis:* "Where did nature find a place in a gnat for all the senses?" We still don't know the full answer, but we can bypass the question: she didn't, she put most of them *on* it; space inside the small bodies of insects is at a premium. On the insect head the convex eye with no true lens has to be broken up into a series of optically isolated tubes represented at the surface by facets, roughly hexagonal in shape. Each tube interprets that part of the visual field towards which it points; collectively they form a mosaic picture.

These simple but profound differences in structure affect vision in many ways. The eyes of mice and men are built on the lines of cameras. They have a lens with iris diaphragm in front to focus the light and control the amount of it, and a concave sensitive surface behind. In between is a space of no biological usefulness. Such an eye cannot cover a field greater than a hemisphere, for reasons of geometry. The insect eye has no such limitation; a dragonfly's field of vision, without moving eye or head, may be limited only by its own tail. It would be nice to be able to drive a car without rear view mirrors. A dragonfly's head is as mobile as any vertebrate's, but its eyes are fixed; Kipling reminds us of the hazard in nature, as in war, in the movement of a vertebrate eye: "And when he could spy the white of her eye, he made the pistol crack."

The eyes of an insect, then, are spread over the surface of its head, or looking at them from the helpful viewpoint of evolution they may be said to flow over the surface of the head, adapting readily in size, shape, and position to the needs of their owners. They may be round or elliptical, egg-shaped or kidney-shaped, or – strangely enough – shaped like tear-drops. In some beetles they have flowed around the bases of the antennae till they engulf these or are divided by them; in others, the whirligig beetles living on the surface of water, each is divided into a lower half for submarine and an upper for aerial vision. Other beetles and some mayflies have all or part of each eye on a periscopic pillar and can see without being seen. Insects, anyhow, always go into things with their eyes open, for they cannot shut them, although it has been claimed that when their subsidiary eyes, the ocelli, are in the dark the compound eyes are neurally "switched off."

Whatever the shape and position of an insect's eyes, their wide fields of view overlap, so that insects share with us the ability to look at things with both eyes. This binocular vision is characteristic of predators and other animals which must have an accurate appreciation of distance, an appreciation which comes from the difference in direction of an object as seen by the right eye and by the left. Imagine the embarrassment of cat or spider that leaps too late at passing prey. Clearly, the accuracy of the estimate will depend on the distance separating the two eyes, a

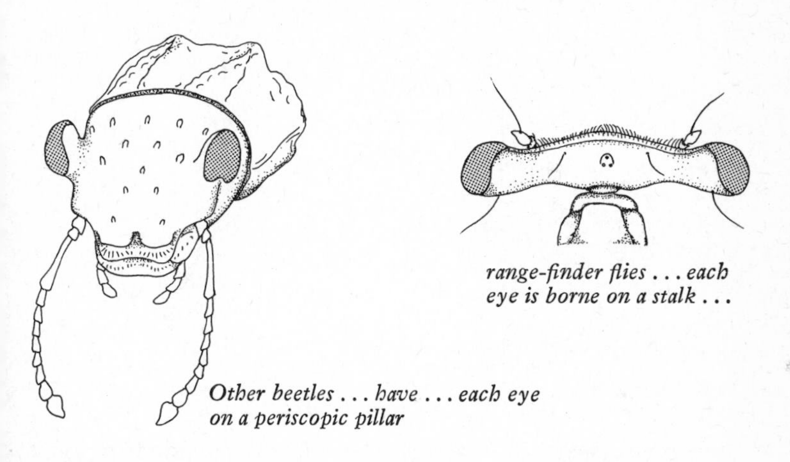

range-finder flies . . . each eye is borne on a stalk . . .

Other beetles . . . have . . . each eye on a periscopic pillar

principle used in range-finders for artillery fire, akin to predation, in which optical means are used to increase the effective separation between the eyes. In the so-called range-finder flies, which are predatory, each eye is borne on a stalk extending sideways from the head.

We pay for our own binocular vision with blindness behind and depend on mobility of eye and neck, or on mirrors, if we would use it askew from dead ahead. Perhaps it is a different kind of blindness behind that leaves us still uncertain whether to thank our predatory or our arboreal past for our binocular vision. Insects' blindness behind is much less than ours, on the average a mere 80°; their pursuers, both insectivores and entomologists, must appreciate this. Insects live in three dimensions and can usually see with both eyes above and below, as well as in front; they have, if you like, altimeter eyes. We should note too, here, that astigmatism is the rule rather than the exception in insects; they can resolve things better in a vertical than in a horizontal plane. This, like their binocular vision above and below, must be helpful in the vertical movements of flight.

an insect's best hope of reading ... moving an eye over the surface of the paper

Insects are so small that they can only accommodate about one visual element for every thousand that we have. How then can insect eyes, in so many directions, out-perform ours? At the terrible price of seeing only very, very poorly wherever they look. A man can see separately two lines a millimeter apart at ten feet; the average insect can only do this at a distance of an inch. But there is no focusing involved in insect vision, no near point within which they cannot focus. An insect's best hope of reading would be in moving an eye over the surface of the paper, letter by letter. Yet this weakness of insect vision accounts in part for two advantages: their eyes adapt well to vision at night, so that many nocturnal insects can see well enough to fly by starlight alone; and they are very sensitive to movement. This last property is made clear if you try to catch a fly by hand; make a grabbing attack directly towards it; or, with both hands approaching directly, one from each side, clap them just above it, allowing for its jumping take off. In this way you may succeed. Move your hand across the field of vision of the fly and you'll be trying till the cows come home.

Insects are colorful things and associate with colorful flowers (p. 139), so that we should expect to find them colour conscious. This is rather difficult to investigate, and so far we have definite proof of an ability to distinguish between colours – by virtue of their colour or wavelength, not their brightness – only for a very small number of insects and for only a very small number of colours.

A quite different though not unrelated matter, the sensitivity of insects to different parts of the spectrum, has been more fully investigated (p. 187). Although in discussing this we shall have to use the names of colours, it must be remembered that we are unlikely ever to know how things appear to insects, and that the ability to see by blue light and by green light does not imply that the two can be distinguished, or that either of them looks blue or green. Our own visual spectrum, the rainbow, extends from the short wavelength violet through to red with about twice its wavelength; that is, about one octave. We are aware of further radiation of longer wavelength than red, although we cannot see it, from the heat its absorption generates. This we call infra-red; its wavelength is longer, its frequency lower. The solar spectrum, until recently the main source of light for insects as well as for us, also extends beyond our visual limit at the violet end, as the ultra-violet. It is not surprising, since space is at such a premium in insects and the minimum size of a visual unit is related to the wavelength it is sensitive to, that the visual spectrum of insects is to the violet side of our own. Many insects are unable to see by red light at all; probably none can see as far into the red as we can. Most, however, can see by ultra-violet, even by wavelengths at this end shorter than any to be found in the solar spectrum by the time it reaches the surface of the earth. Why should insects be sensitive to radiation to which they are not exposed? Again we must turn to evolution for the answer; insects are a very ancient group; when the visual pigments in their eyes were evolved the earth was an altogether different place. The ozone layer in the atmosphere which now screens out this short-wave ultra-violet did not then exist. Short-wave ultra-violet did indeed reach the earth's surface at that time. The ozone layer has developed since as oxygen in the air has increased.

Ultra-violet is strong medicine as anybody knows who has fallen asleep in the sun. Many microorganisms are killed by a short exposure to the wavelengths to which insect eyes are sensitive. Indeed, it may well be that the pigment which enables insects to see by this wavelength, and which must of course absorb it, evolved originally as a protection against it. Such protection is accorded by sea water, to which most earlier living things were confined.

Our eyes are most sensitive to light in the yellow region of the spectrum; those of insects examined so far mostly show two peaks of sensitivity, one in the ultra-violet and one in the blue-green region. There is some indirect evidence that most insects distinguish these two regions as different "insect colours," but we, denied this sensitivity, have no way of guessing what ultra-violet looks like to an insect.

Part of the puzzle over the colours of flowers and the scanty evidence of good colour vision in insects may be answered by this different sensitivity. The colours we see in flowers may be accidental, or incidental, to their true colours as displayed for insects. We may see a flower as a brilliant red because a pigment in it which reflects ultra-violet also, incidentally, reflects red. A uniformly drab flower to us may be to an insect a daringly patterned two-tone creation.

The most incredible attribute of insect eyes seems to depend on a structural feature only revealed by electron microscopy. In the six or eight cells which make up the sensitive surfaces underlying each facet are fine lamellae, differently oriented in each cell. These, it seems, enable an insect to distinguish the plane of polarization of light. Most light is made up of vibrations in a mixture of directions, all at right angles to the direction of travel of the light. Reflection from some surfaces, scatter in the sky, and passage through certain crystals and other transparent materials favour vibrations in a particular plane, or "polarize" the light. This looks no different to us unless we examine it with an optical instrument designed for the purpose. Insects have such an optical instrument built into their eyes. Since the plane of polarization of light from the sky depends on its position in relation to the sun, insects can get their bearings from any fragment of blue sky visible on a miserable day, whether or no it could keep a sailor decent. The hive bee can do this to within 3°; this is better direction finding than many of us can manage with a pocket compass. There is room for endless speculation as to what north might look like to a bee.

With this as background, can we now put ourselves inside the head of an insect and ". . . see oursels as ithers see us?" We seem to have learnt a lot, yet many of the more important points remain a mystery to us. We must try to interpret what we do know from the insect viewpoint, a little viewpoint, as Walter de la Mare says:

> *How large unto the tiny fly,*
> *Must little things appear! –*
> *A rosebud like a feather-bed,*
> *Its prickle like a spear;*
>
> *(The Fly)*

This verse also suggests the essential difference, the size difference, between the world of insects and that of men. Each goes about its daily business largely oblivious of the other. Each doubtless views itself as master of its environment, the one looking at it as a mosaic, close-up, short-sightedly; the other, also short-sightedly, as a present possession. Each is equally wrong. Each, we must hope, will continue to learn, in the evolutionary sense, from the other.

THE VARIETY OF INSECTS

In which the poets tell of the diversity of insects as a whole, and accounts of the four grand orders illustrate something of diversity at lower levels. First, the most abundant, the beetles; then the most spectacular, the butterflies and moths; then two tales each on some reputedly misanthropic flies and philanthropic wasps and bees.

8

Verses to Order

SO MANY and varied are the insects that we have to divide them into smaller groups to understand this variety. The smallest group which the man in the street can be counted on to recognize is the order: insects such as the beetles (ch. 9), the moths and butterflies (ch. 10), the flies proper, and improper (ch. 11 and 12), and the bees, wasps, and ants (ch. 13 and 14) are orders. The insects are a class of the animal kingdom, that is to say a group two steps down from the kingdom; step one, the phylum the arthropods (ch. 2), including crustaceans and millipedes and spiders and scorpions, step two the class, Insecta. An order is another step down from the class, and a step up from a family.

Louis Agassiz's aphorism that a phylum is an idea and a class a way of expressing that idea, applies as well to a class and its constituent orders, particularly so to the insects. Opinions differ as to the number of insect orders which should be recognized, ranging from 2 dozen to 3 dozen; I shall refer only to the 18 most likely to be familiar to you. Many books are available which list the insect orders along with the structural features that distinguish them. I want to give a somewhat more lively account of these lively animals and shall make use of the wings of song and verse to keep before you the all important point that most insects fly. But first, a few that don't.

Many insects, mostly all too familiar ones like bed bugs, have lost their wings, but there are still a few in existence that have not yet got around to evolving any. Some of these still have remnants of legs on their abdomens, helping us to understand the origins of insects. There is one group with bristle-like filaments on their tails, hence their latin name. Thysanura, meaning simply that they have *thysanos* or bristles on their *ura* or tails, although you probably know them as:

Silverfish, sliverfish, hot from the furnace room,*
Asbestos bug, firebrat, hurrying to hide;
What is the link to your halophile cousins that
Scurry on shore line 'twixt low and high tide?
Up from the ages, successful in winglessness,
Thanks for your clues to the source of your class.
Abdominal styles, and heuristic appendages;
Dance you male firebrat, make love to your lass.

Far more outlandish and somewhat less familiar are the springtails or snowfleas, whose latin name is Collembola because they have *kollos* or glue on their *embolon*, a peg-like projection under the abdomen. This peg holds them in place on the surface of water, from which, however, they can leap by releasing their tails from underneath themselves in a spring-like manner.

Purple grey scum-patch with leaping propensities,
Urbanizations on snow pools in spring,
Answer the challenge of those who deny to you
Membership proud, in the Hexapod ring.

Show your six legs and your wonderful tagmata,
Draw a scale veil o'er your abdomen queer;
Numberless numbers in soils of the centuries,
To waters ahead may your glue-pegs adhere.

• • • •

And now to that all important point, that most insects fly – but many of the more primitive winged insects have largely escaped

* This is not a misprint.

the attention of poets, including, it seems, the Ephemeroptera or mayflies, delicatessen of fish. I know but two fragments referring to them:

The sun comes forth, and many reptiles spawn;
He sets, and each ephemeral insect then
Is gathered into death without a dawn,
And the immortal stars awake again;
(Shelley: in *Adonais*)

Not a bee shall hear him creeping,
Not a may-fly shall awaken,
From its crad'ling blue-bell shaken,
(Shelley: in *Wake the Serpent Not*)

Insects which as adults intrude so briefly upon us call for further notice:

Months
As aquatic edition of silverfish, of fish the food;
Then a brief life aerial.
Wings why embarrassingly unfoldable,
Yet surprisingly moultable?
Quick iridescent courtship dance,
Get back with eggs
To feed
Your fish.

The Odonata, dragonflies and damselflies, make the move from water to air in Tennyson's *The Two Voices:*

'Today I saw the dragon-fly
Come from the wells where he did lie.

'An inner impulse rent the veil
Of his old husk; from head to tail
Came out clear plates of sapphire mail.

'He dried his wings: like gauze they grew;
Through crofts and pastures wet with dew
A living shaft of light he flew.'

Landor tells a different tale:

. . . . by the running stream,
Brimful of moral, where the Dragon-fly
Wanders as careless and content as I.

Thanks for this fancy, insect king,
Of purple crest and filmy wing,
Who with indifference givest up
The water-lily's golden cup;
To come again and overlook
What I am writing in my book.
Believe me, most who read the line
Will read with hornier eyes than thine;
And yet their souls shall live for ever,
And thine drop dead into the river!
God pardon them, O insect king,
Who fancy so unjust a thing!
(W. S. Landor: in *The Dragon-fly*)

Out on to dry land again, to the Orthoptera – in the broad sense. These ancient insects have inspired much poetry, with the lion's share going to the musical and saltatorial grasshoppers and crickets. One of the gems in this musical story is Leigh Hunt's sonnet; what form could be more appropriate for a grasshopper's little song?

Green little vaulter in the sunny grass,
Catching your heart up at the feel of June,
Sole voice that's heard amidst the lazy noon,
When even the bees lag at the summoning brass;
And you, warm little housekeeper, who class
With those who think the candles come too soon,

Loving the fire, and with your tricksome tune
Nick the glad silent moments as they pass;
Oh sweet and tiny cousins, that belong,
One to the fields, the other to the hearth,
Both have your sunshine; both, though small, are strong
At your clear hearts; and both seem given to earth
To sing in thoughtful ears this natural song –
Indoors and out, summer and winter, Mirth.
(*The Grasshopper and the Cricket*)

Written on the spot in rivalry with Keats' sonnet of the same title, this is the better both as entomology and as poetry.

Don Marquis' charming archy has done something to offset the overemphasis on the musicians and redeem the reputation of the roaches:

i wish you would have mehitabel kill that rat
or get a cat that is onto her job
and i will write you a series of poems showing how
things look
to a cockroach
that rat s name is freddy
the next time freddy dies i hope he won t be a rat
but something smaller i hope i will be a rat
in the next transmigration and freddy a cockroach
i will teach him to sneer at my poetry then

don t you ever eat any sandwiches in your office
i haven t had a crumb of bread for i don t know how long
or a piece of ham or anything but apple parings
and paste leave a piece of paper in your machine
every night you can call me archy
(in *archy and mehitabel*)

The maverick order Dermaptera is most familiarly represented by the earwigs. These can scarcely be called poetical insects, and they are treated without a trace of poetic license by Thomas Hood:

The key-hole lodged the ear-wig and her brood.
The emmets of the steps had old possession,
And marched in search of their diurnal food
In undisturbed procession.

(in *The Haunted House*)

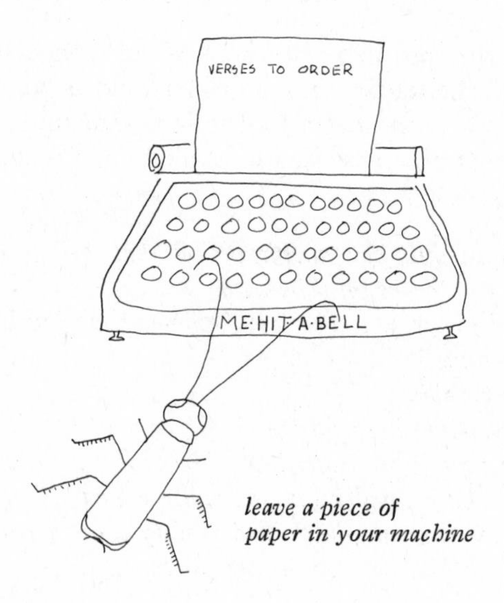

leave a piece of paper in your machine

Tis vain to talk of hopes and fears
and hope the least reply to win,
From any maid that stops her ears
In dread of ear-wigs creeping in!

(in *Love Lane*)

and more recently but no less realistically, in a fragment from Fay Inchfawn:

And when a fat brown earwig drops
Suddenly down my neck and stops.
I can't help screaming.

"Them's no harm
at all", says Michael.
(in *I'm Very Fond of Gardening*)

The Isoptera, the white ants or termites, partake of some of the characteristics of the earwigs, but archy would have seen in them the dangers of a cockroach welfare state. It was Ogden Nash who put the economic aspect of these insects in a nutshell:

Some primal termite knocked on wood
And tasted it, and found it good,
And that is why your Cousin May
Fell through the parlor floor today.
(*The Termite*)

Now had Cousin May been a bookworm, she might have accepted her fate philosophically and been thankful that she was dealing with termites and not with bookworms of another kind: representatives of the Psocoptera, who once had wings but sold their birthright for a mess of paper. These insects are more properly known as booklice, but the name bookworm has been used indiscriminately for many animals that burrow in books, from beetle grubs to people. One would not perhaps expect the bookworms to attract much attention from poets, but there are several verses written to one or another of these animals. There is nothing in these lines attributed to Evenus to indicate that he was not thinking of true booklice, representatives of this minor order:

Page-eater thou, the Muses' bitterest foe,
Hidden destroyer, feeding constantly
On stolen wisdom, why, black worm, lurk low
In holy works, emblem of jealousy?

Far from the Muses fly! And do not show
The envious tip of thy sharp probe to me –

and from Norman Douglas' *Birds and Beasts of the Greek Anthology*, a reply to it:

Quoth the bookworm, "I don't care a bit
If the writer has wisdom or wit.
A volume must be
Pretty tough to bore me
As completely as I can bore it."

One of our common species today bears the specific name *divinatorius*, it being most commonly found in Bibles. These insects are said to thrive on molds growing on the glue and sizing in undisturbed places; our reading habits do not seem to have changed much since the Greeks.

The Anoplura, the true lice, have drawn poetic invective, mostly directed, alas, at the human body louse; understandable since no other species, perhaps, feeds so commonly on poets. Robbie Burns ploughed into them properly, if somewhat undemocratically, with his:

Ye ugly creepin', blastit wonner,
Detested, shunn'd by saunt an' sinner,
How dare yet set your fit upon her,
Sae fine a lady?
Gae somewhere else, and seek your dinner,
On some poor body.
(in *To a Louse, on seeing one on a lady's bonnet at church*)

A more balanced viewpoint, naturally, is expressed by archy:

a louse i
used to know
told me that
millionaires and
bums tasted
about alike
to him

(Don Marquis: in *the lives and times of archy and mehitabel*)

Other animals have lice too, fascinating parasites which might have been viewed more objectively but have been ignored, save by an anonymous prayer writer of the 19th century, who included an assortment of other insects related to the lice only by their habits in this catch-all plea:

From red-bugs and bed-bugs, from sand-flies and land-flies,
Mosquitoes, gallinippers and fleas,
From hog-ticks and dog-ticks, from hen-lice and men-lice,
We pray thee, good Lord, give us ease.

(*An old Prayer* : circa 1856)

A comparable prayer on behalf of flowers would certainly have had to cover the Thysanoptera or thrips, midget fringed-winged insects which must surely represent the epitome of irritation in the crevices of the flowers they inhabit. They deserve a verse, if but a short one, but most poets have overlooked the thrips. William Cullen Bryant mentioned them, but succumbed to the temptation to drop the final "s." As if to compensate for its small size, one of these insects is properly referred to as a thrip*s*:

The army worm and the Hessian fly
And the dreaded canker-worm shall die,
And the thrip and the slug and the fruit moth seek
In vain to escape that busy beak,
And fairer harvests shall crown the year,
For the Old-World sparrow at last is here.

(in *The Old-World Sparrow*)

An unfortunate forecast as things have turned out, as Bryant seems to have realized, for he added a note: "I hope I have not said too much for the sparrow."

Our prayer writer recognized the bedbug, a true but degenerate bug representative of the order Hemiptera. The true bugs have had slim pickings from the poets, as indeed have the other half of the order, with one exception, the cicadas. These elusive insects are often confused with grasshoppers or crickets who also, like determined poets, insist on being heard. From the Greeks to the moderns the cicadas have drawn comment:

Happy the cicadas' lives
For they all have voiceless wives

is ascribed to Xenarchus and may appeal to my male readers. For the moderns, Aldous Huxley emphasizes the voices of the males:

For like inveterate remorse, like shrill
Delirium throbbing in the fevered brain,
An unseen people of cicadas fill
Night with their one harsh note, again, again.
Again, again, with what insensate zest!
What fury of persistence, hour by hour!
Filled with what demon that denies them rest,
Drunk with what source of pleasure and of power!
Life is their madness, life that all night long
Bids them to sing and sing, they know not why;
(in *The Cicadas*)

A shot-gun fired into a tree full of them will silence them, but only momentarily. Perhaps it is well that some of them only produce adults once in seventeen years.

The aphids, as prodigal of offspring as the male cicada is of song, have received passing mention from Charles Darwin's grandfather:

The countless Aphides, prolific tribe
With greedy trunks the honey's sap imbibe;
Swarm on each leaf with eggs or embryons big,
And pendant nations tenant every twig.
(Erasmus Darwin: in *Origin of Society*)

. . . .

We turn now to the dominant group of insects, those in which the infants are so unlike their parents that the relationship can only be detected with the help of inside information. Tennyson's verse on a dragonfly foreshadowed this. Included here are the four grand orders, the beetles, the butterflies and moths, the flies, and the bees and their relatives. The first three of these have minor orders which are in varying degree related to them.

Much of the verse on the grand orders such as the beetles – and there is plenty – is well enough known that we can restrict ourselves to instructive tit-bits.

On the Coleoptera themselves James Whitcomb Riley emphasizes the noisy, rather clumsy, crepuscular flight of large beetles (ch. 9):

O'er folded blooms,
On swirls of musk,
The beetle booms adown the glooms
And bumps along the dusk.
(in *Dusk Song – The Beetle*)

By contrast there is this tribute to the elegance of tiny ones:

The shapely limb and lubricated joint,
Within the small dimensions of a point.
(cited in Taylor, see p. 188)

Few poets have been able to resist at least a passing allusion to glowworms or fireflies, and most of us now meet ladybird beetles in verse in the nursery long before we meet them in the flesh.

The Neuroptera as we now know them, regarded by some as ancestrally connected to the beetles, include the lace-wings and the ant-lions as I think their only representatives noticed by poets; not that the rest are unpoetical or uninspiring. It was the eggs of the lace-wings, and of white ants, which called forth:

The lace-wing fly Chrysopa
Lays each egg on a stalk,
The larva has to climb down this
Before it starts to walk.

Ten million eggs one termite lays
But most of them lay none.
They work as nursemaids all their days,
And don't get any fun.

The doodlebugs or ant-lions, (p. 170) larvae of other Neuroptera whose dragonfly-like adults have no common name, inspired Madison Cawein's poem *Old Snake-Doctor:*

Once I found an ant-lion's hole
And an ant-lion in it: nippers
Like a pair of rusty clippers.
And I saw a red ant roll
In its pit, and, quick as Ned,
This old ant-lion fanged its head,
Held it till the ant was dead.
(in *The Giant and the Star*)

The Lepidoptera, the moths and butterflies, originated in association with the caddis-flies, the Trichoptera. Their wing scales, which enrapture the poets, are no more than the flattened hairs of this minor group which poets have almost ignored. The only lines to the Trichoptera I know of are from Christopher Smart's *Rejoice with the Lamb:*

Let Mibzar rejoice with the Cadess, as is their number so are their names, blessed be the Lord Jesus for them all.
For the names and number of animals are as the names and number of the stars.

Smart also gives us in the same work an unusual slant on the silkworm (p. 107) and hence on caterpillars in general, and also on the butterflies transformed from them:

Let Huldah bless with the Silkworm – the ornaments of the Proud are from the bowells of their Betters.
Let Susanna bless with the Butterfly – beauty hath wings, but chastity is the Cherub.

Tennyson has recorded the reactions of moths to light:

Thy moth will singe her wings, and singed return,
Her love of light quenching her fear of pain.
(in *Sir John Oldcastle*)

and Swinburne the migration of butterflies over the sea (pp. 44, 108):

Fly, white butterflies, out to sea.
Frail pale wings for the winds to try;
Small white wings that we scarce can see,
Fly.
(in *White Butterflies*)

The least poetical of the grand orders is the Diptera, the two-winged flies, amongst these are distributed verses reflecting man's attitude of hate, not unmixed with fear, as that by Karl Shapiro:

But I, a man, must swat you with my hate,
Slap you across the air and crush your flight,
Must mangle with my shoe and smear your blood,
Expose your little guts pasty and white,

Knock your head sidewise like a drunkard's hat,
Pin your wings under like a crow's
Tear off your flimsy clothes
And beat you as one beats a rat.

(in *The Fly*)

Certain Maxims by Don Marquis' archy are refreshing by contrast:

a man thinks
he amounts to a lot
but to a mosquito
a man is
merely
something to eat

The fleas, or Siphonaptera, a minor order related to the flies, have attracted poets out of all proportion to their numbers. Or could it be that poets have attracted fleas?

A poet's song can memorize a flea;
The subtle fancy of deep-witted Donne
The wee phlebotomist descanted on . . .
Pasquier, the gravest joker of the age,
Berhymed LaPuce in many a polished page.
(Coleridge: cited in Twinn, see p. 188)

Subtle fancy and deep witted to be sure, Donne's is one of the finest of insect poems:

Mark but this flea, and mark in this,
How little that which thou deny'st me is;
It sucked me first, and now sucks thee,
And in this flea, our two bloods mingled be;
Thou know'st that this cannot be said
A sin, nor shame, nor loss of maidenhead,
Yet this enjoys before it woo,
And pampered swells with one blood made of two,
And this, alas, is more than we would do.

Oh stay, three lives in one flea spare,
Where we almost, yea more than married are.
This flea is you and I, and this
Our marriage bed, and marriage temple is;
Though parents grudge, and you, we're met,
And cloistered in these living walls of jet.
Though use make you apt to kill me,
Let not to that, self murder added be,
And sacrilege, three sins in killing three.

Cruel and sudden, hast thou since
Purpled thy nail, in blood of innocence:
Wherein could this flea guilty be,
Except in that drop which it sucked from thee?
Yet thou triumph'st, and say'st that thou
Find'st not thyself, nor me the weaker now;
'Tis true, then learn how false, fears be;
Just so much honour, when thou yield'st to me,
Will waste, as this flea's death took life from thee.
(*The Flea*)

Christopher Smart adds a penetrating contribution:

Let Ethan praise with the Flea, his coat of mail, his piercer, and his vigour, which wisdom and providence have contrived to attract observation and to escape it.
(in *Jubilate Agno*)

Among the Hymenoptera a single species, the hive bee, has had more verse written about it than any other insect; the ants, too, have been lavishly but less well treated; the wasps, and especially the sawflies, ichneumon flies, and related parasites have been scarcely mentioned.

Aristophanes held up the wasps as examples of litigiousness; Edmund Blunden gave them excellent scientific treatment in his *Perch-fishing:*

And there the wasps, that lodge them ill-concealed
In the vole's empty house, still drove afield
To plunder touchwood from old crippled trees
And build their young ones their hutched nurseries;

Erasmus Darwin, Charles' grandfather, gives a succinct account of a characteristic activity of ichneumon flies in his *Origin of Society:*

The wing'd Ichneumon for the embryon young
Gores with sharp horn the caterpillar throng,
The cruel larva mines its silky course,
And tears the vitals of its fostering nurse.

And a remarkable item on the bee is the anticipation by Andrew Marvell in his *The Garden* of the discoveries of von Frisch, some three hundred years later:

And, as it works, th' industrious Bee
Computes its time as well as we.

Thus may poetic insight precede scientific verification.

A remarkable procession, these eighteen orders, and a remarkable gathering of poets that have responded to them. Perhaps more remarkable still are the gems that I have had to leave out. Could it have been the six feet that beguiled the poets? – but little of the output is in hexameters.

9

With Beetling Brows

HOW is a brow, when it beetles? Or to put it differently, how is a beetle? For these two words mean the same thing – to stick out or project. And if there is one group of insects which sticks out from all others, it is the beetles. Some authorities hold that the word beetle is of common origin with the verb to bite, but since what one bites with must, at least at the time of biting, stick out, it may be that all three words have the same source. As the insects are the most numerous kinds of animals so the beetles are the most numerous insects, and the weevils, incidentally, are the most numerous beetles. Something over 300,000 species of beetles have

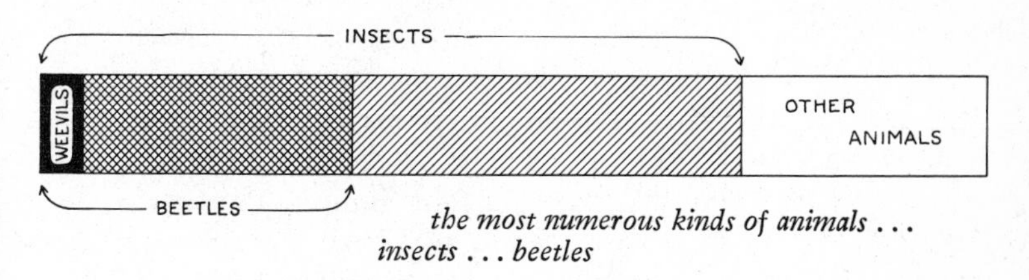

the most numerous kinds of animals . . . insects . . . beetles

been described and something over 40,000 species of weevils; these figures make them respectively the largest natural order and the largest natural family of living things. God must indeed have loved the beetles to have made so many of them. And who wouldn't?

Perhaps the most engaging trait of these most armoured of insects is the confidence this armour seems to give them, and it is this in turn which makes them stick out. For though mostly slow to fly and indifferent performers in the air, they are often active in broad daylight. And though generally secretive, like all insects, they are often to be seen secreted within nothing but their own armour. What is this armour? Qualitatively it is much like the body covering of any other insect, though generally thicker, harder, often darker, and certainly more generously provided. Like any insect a beetle gets its flexibility from the elastic parts of the body covering which connect one rigid plate to the next, but in beetles these flexible parts are cut down to an irreducible minimum and folded inwards wherever possible between plates. But above all else the most striking peculiarity of their armour is that they have devoted the first of their two hard-won pairs of wings to the protective function, a surprising sacrifice.

If wings have made the insects such successful animals, why should sacrificing a pair make the beetles such successful insects? In part, perhaps, because sacrificing the first pair is an insurance against damaging the second, over which the first forms a rigid, closely interlocking sheath, the *coleos* of Coleoptera, meeting together in one of the neatest outside joints in the animal kingdom and forming the most distinctive badge of a beetle, a straight line down the back. Perhaps this has something to do with their common name, too, for flying by flapping the hind pair of wings only does give an insect the appearance of projecting in front. The front wings are held open at an angle by the flying beetle so that, although they do not flap, they do contribute to lift and stability.

Beetles, for the most part, feed as did their ancestors with three conservative pairs of jaws sticking out somewhat in front or below the head. These are visible projections, clearly designed for biting and manipulating solid food. The first jaws are as hard and solid as the rest of a beetle's body covering: they are the offensive part of the armour, and beetles clearly accept the military maxim that attack is the best form of defence. They will use their jaws against almost anything, without regard to race, colour, creed or calling.

Many a tiger beetle lives to bite again through biting the grabbing hand of an unwary entomologist. The other end of a beetle is not without its aggressive armour either. The spurs on the hind legs of a giant water beetle cause many a captor's hand to relax when they are stuck out into a tender palm.

The chemical armoury of beetles includes the repellent, the caustic, and the corrosive; butyric acid, phenolic compounds, formic acid, and ammonia. All are secreted by beetle glands and released or even projected against attackers of beetles. The most striking performance in this direction is that of the bombardier beetles. Into a small chamber at the rear end they secrete a mixture of hydroquinones; to this is added hydrogen peroxide, resulting in an explosive release of oxygen which projects, with an appropriately audible report, droplets of the caustic mixture to a distance of up to ten times the length of the beetle. The hungriest of insectivores lose their appetites for insects when this miniature stink bomb is released squarely into a mouth opened in readiness for a tasty crunch of beetle. And this rear gunner has at his immediate command passable markmanship and a magazine of 20 shots.

How can one stand out when one is only a quarter of a millimeter long? Difficult I'll agree, but the Trichopterygids, among the smallest of all beetles and smaller than some protozoa, do at least have fringes of hair standing out all around their wings. At the other end of the scale, among the rhinoceros and hercules beetles, the names are enough to tell us how their brows beetle; they have, as the saying goes, at least one bodger on the bonce and commonly some elsewhere. These are such striking decorations that, in mentioning the size of these beetles, it is important to specify whether they are included; the male of *Dynastes hercules* of central America is best described, for example, as measuring 15.9 centimetres *with bodger*. It is, indeed, more bodger than beetle. The weight of the greatest beetle is perhaps fifty million times that of the least; between the least and the greatest there are also perhaps half a million undiscovered species awaiting description. These have, all of them, the distinctive badges of beetles, but each has also special characteristics of its own.

In general terms, perhaps the best impression one can give of this diversity of beetledom is to liken it to an explosion of evolution. In structure and habits the beetles have evolved in so many directions that they seem to have been spun outwards from a centrifuge of chance. To get a real understanding of this complex diversity calls for a lifetime of study; all we can do here is to sketch a few models. But before doing this, we must add a new dimension to the picture, that of time. Every beetle as we know it is an adult male or female, usually with roughly equal probability. Occasionally, as in the engraver beetle *Xyleborus fornicatus*, the chances of encountering a male may be reduced, as the name perhaps suggests, even to as low as one in two hundred. And every adult is preceded by three immature stages, egg, grub, and pupa, each more numerous than the one which follows it, extending back as far as fifteen years into the past. Beetle eggs are rather ordinary insect eggs, mostly white or pale, smooth, and ellipsoid, but grubs take many forms as they develop, even the grubs of the same species. They have obvious heads with mouthparts, showing a rudimentary resemblance to those of their parents, and three pairs of not overly competent legs. Most find a pair of leg-like structures on the tail end a valuable supplement to lever the somewhat fleshy abdomen along in pursuit of the more agile front end. But weevil grubs, living inside plants and their seeds, find most of these things superfluous and can afford to be fleshy all over. The pupa of a beetle – a beetle pup – looks somewhat like a hunched up human fetus, but with the rudimentary legs and wings of the adult beetle clearly showing. Some distinguished coleopterists have taken on something of this appearance towards the end of their days, much as, they say, a man and his dog come to resemble each other.

Between them, beetles eat almost anything that is edible, but there is a large, somewhat primitive group restricted to carnivorous diets. Some of these are aquatic, both as grubs and adults, and eat anything from mosquito larvae to small fish. The jaws of the grubs are grooved and project threateningly. They penetrate the prey and digestive fluid passes into it. After an appropriate interval the now liquified contents of the prey are sucked back through the grooves and the empty skin is discarded. The adults are handsome ovoid diving beetles with hind legs flattened and fringed with hair for swimming. They have more normal jaws and can thus be raised on fragments of raw meat or liver, which they eat politely. Urbanization has been unkind to these pond dwellers. It has been their wont in the fall of the year to take long flights at night to establish themselves in other lakes and ponds, recognizing these by the light of the moon which the water surfaces reflect, and diving headlong into them. Before cities grew, light shining upwards could only mean water below; now, as often as not it means street lights and sidewalks. It is well that beetles are armoured. The Chinese find the large species good to eat and will take advantage of their temporary confusion after impact to gather them for this purpose. Other people fail to see them, or comment on their stupidity, perhaps forgetting how stupid they would feel themselves after diving into an empty swimming pool.

There are other quite unrelated water beetles with a superficial resemblance to the diving beetles; but most of them feed on rotting vegetation, and they can be distinguished by their clubbed antennae, which they use in a strange breathing procedure, for none of these beetles have gills. The antenna is used to break the surface tension and hold a channel open for replenishment of the air supplies. In nature these beetles can be recognized much more readily by the slower stroke they swim, moving their hind legs alternately. The diving beetles swim by moving both hind legs together, and when they fall on their backs they use this same action to get turned over. This is a much older requirement for beetleness than swimming; perhaps these beetles first learned to swim by accident, falling on their backs into water.

The difficulty most beetles have in turning over when upside down is a conspiracy between rotundity and armour. It is a difficulty which has evidently been quite important in their evolution since special devices have been developed to deal with it. Some beetles open their wing covers to get turned over, but the most spectacular device is that of the click beetles. They can be recognized at once by a transverse hinge across their middles which keeps them flexible, even in old age. Turn them over, and spanning this hinge will be found a little hook and socket catch which is used to hold them bent for a few moments when they are on their backs while appropriate muscular tensions are built up. The catch is released with a click, and the back of the beetle strikes the ground and throws it into the air, with a better than even chance of coming down right side up. And if it fails it tries again. If these beetles are turned over on the bottoms of tin cans the click is greatly amplified, an arrangement which lends itself well to juvenile gambling activities in which many an allowance has changed hands. The grubs of some of the click beetles are the wireworms of agricultural notoriety, but this need not interfere with the sport since it takes populations of several million per acre before their damage attracts attention.

Some tropical click beetles have luminous organs like a pair of glowing eyes on the back of the thorax and are among our most spectacular fireflies. The brightest species emit one thirty-eighth of a candle power. The glowworms of more temperate regions are the wingless females of a quite different group of beetles. Their grubs feed on snails and slugs in a manner very similar to that of the diving beetle. In many luminous insects both sexes glow, and the light is said to assist the coming together of the beetle sexes; to judge from poets, male and female, it may have a similar effect in other species. We are some way yet from understanding the full significance of these strange cold lights.

The oil beetles, so called from the oily fluid secreted from their joints when they are handled, lay up to ten thousand eggs. Whenever an animal lays a fabulous number of eggs one can look for something of peculiar interest in its life history. For example, lively little larvae with an extra claw on each foot hatch from these eggs, on or under the ground, and may make their way up into a recently opened flower. There they sit pacifically awaiting with peculiar interest the appearance of a leg, which must be both female and hairy and belong to a particular species of bee. The signal for the arrival of this specific leg lies in the buzz of the bee, to the peculiar note of which the larva responds by rearing up on the six-clawed tiptoes of its hind legs and grappling hopefully with a pair of peculiarly serrated mandibles. In these mandibles lies an additional safeguard against catching the wrong bee bus, for the serrations fit precisely the hairs of the right bee, and her unwitting function is to carry the larva back to her nest. Here, when an egg drops from the bee the larva drops with it, to be sealed up in the cell along with the provisions for nourishing the bee grub. Having secured these provisions for itself by eating the bee's egg, the larva moults to an inactive fleshy form more suitable for floating around on the honey, its next meal. It may then moult to a legless form before finally pupating, later to emerge as perhaps a male oil beetle who will make his way out of the bee's nest to find a female oil beetle. At this point he must grapple for her antennae with a peculiar notch on his own, much as he grappled as an infant for the hairy leg of the female bee.

And so we could go on and on; the leaf beetles and the longhorns, both wearing a heart on each foot as a whimsical change from one on a sleeve. The leaf beetles are as broad as they are long, rotund, small, and flea-like or larger and brightly striped. The longhorns are long in the body, but the sweeping calliper-curve of the still longer antennae seems to suggest that they might be used to measure the diameter of trees. And well they might be, for this is where the eggs are laid and the grubs chew their growth tunnels. The ladybirds, round and be-spotted and more be-rhymed than any other beetles, with the help of their larvae do more than all the chemists in Christendom to keep the lousiness of plants within bounds. These taxonomic anomalies are also known as ladybugs, ladycows, ladyflies, and ladybeetles; even the males.

The striking orange and black sexton beetles and the unobtrusive hide beetles do more between them to clean up the colossal carcasses which vertebrates leave around when they die than any other insects, save perhaps the blowflies. The scarabs and dung beetles clean up the piles of dung which the vertebrates, either from laziness or indifference, leave around while they are alive. They invented the wheel to do so, rolling the dung into balls which they trundle away between their hind legs like animated wheelbarrows, to bury them as food for their young. It was largely on this account that the scarabs were accorded the symbolism of creation five thousand years ago in the valley of the

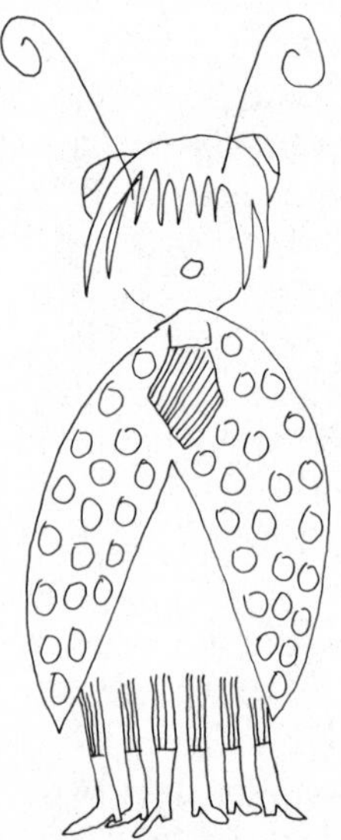

indifferent performers in the air

Nile. Their fossilized dung balls have been dug up in India and mistaken for cannonballs, a later and less laudable human invention.

And finally, since even beetles must come to an end, let us

return to where we began, with a word about the weevils whose brows beetle beyond comprehension, for the snout that characterizes a weevil, unlike most other snouts in insects, is a part of the head itself, though it may be three times as long, and still carries mouthparts on its end. It curves the opposite way to the bodger of the rhinoceros and may be used by females to drill holes in seeds for the reception of eggs. There is an Indian weevil, with a grub the size of my thumb, that feeds in the growing shoots of bamboos. These may grow a foot in a night, and the grub must tunnel as fast or die for lack of the nutrients the tip provides. A third organism is involved: man eats the grub and in seeking it ruins more bamboo shoots than the weevil does. There is also an African weevil that goes in and out of an ants' nest through a hole the size of a period on this page.

10

Scales, Straws, and Silk

AFTER a hunger-making day in the field last summer, I was eating in a country restaurant when a tiny white pillar sticking up straight from a cabbage leaf on my plate caught my eye. It was finely sculpted in a delicate pattern, reminiscent of one in white marble at Fatehpur Sikri. At this point I noticed that a waitress who had eyed my haversack and net suspiciously when I came in had fixed me with an uncompromising look, so I decided, the cabbage being reasonably well cooked, that discretion was the better part of valour and I downed it, chewing perhaps somewhat more thoroughly than I am accustomed to. Good digestion did indeed wait upon appetite.

consume cabbage at . . . speed

Had the cabbage leaf been spared the pot a little longer, from the tiny pillar in white would have hatched a tiny caterpillar in green, known to those who abhor latin as an imported cabbage worm. Imported refers to the worm rather than to the cabbage.

These caterpillars grow rapidly and consume cabbage at about the speed that I consumed mine, moulting as they grow. When this is done and the cabbage patch annihilated, they migrate away from the remains of it and up onto the lee side of a fence post or a tree, or under a windowsill or drip-cap of house or barn. There each spins for itself a button of silk at the tail end, below, and a girdle of silk like a steeplejack's strap around its middle, before transforming into an oddly angular chrysalis. Then to wait. Through the long winter there is no sign of life, but with the warmth of spring the chrysalis ruptures and a cabbage white butterfly, the adult of an imported cabbage worm, works its way out. Then after expanding its wings and seeking its complementary sex, and after feeding on nectar at available flowers, the female of the pair seeks out a new cabbage patch to deposit, during her characteristic dipping flight, another scattered series of tiny white pillars.

This tale of the life of a butterfly has been familiar from times long past to cabbage growers in the Old World, and since 1880 to people with similar interests in the New. This species was imported from the Old World in 1859 and, moving much faster than man, arrived in California 27 years later.

I should perhaps mention at this point that there is an uncommon condition, referred to in medical jargon as scoleciasis, in which the human gut houses living caterpillars. The term scoleciasis should properly be restricted to an infestation with tapeworms, but that no other term has been coined for this other condition serves to emphasize that is it not common. Interestingly, the commonest caterpillar involved is our friend the imported cabbage worm, taking up residence presumably when its host eats raw or undercooked cabbage, and maintained by his continuing to do so in uncommon amounts. So perhaps it is well to notice tiny white pillars – or tiny green caterpillars – on cabbage leaves, and give them an extra chew in passing. So far as I know, these caterpillars never mature on the lee side of the stomach or on the wall of the large intestine, so that the expression 'butterflies in the stomach' remains no more than a metaphor, at least as regards living ones. But people do, from time to time, eat butterflies to see what they taste like, and the so-called bugong moths are a staple item in the diet of some primitive Australian tribes. Most butterflies are reputedly free to fly by day by virtue of being unpalatable, while tasty moths must confine their activities to night time.

Of all the orders of insects none have their beauty more widely appreciated nor more celebrated in verse and song than the moths and butterflies. This beauty is only skin deep, or perhaps I should say scale deep; almost all the coloration and pattern of moths and butterflies is a mosaic of colored scales developed from the surface of the body and wings in overlapping lines like the shingles on a house, pointing in the direction of air flow over them in flight. In the smaller and more primitive moths, brown, buff, white, and grey scales predominate, with occasional patches of metallic bronze or black; in the butterflies, the hawk moths, and the saturnids the scales may be brilliantly pigmented in orange, yellow, or red or give metallic reflections of intense blue, green, or purple. But though scales give them their name, Lepidoptera – the scaly wings – they are not the prerogative of the butterflies and moths. Fish and reptiles have them, and among the insects many weevils, mosquitoes, and even the lowly silverfish are so adorned. We must look then for other things to be sure that we know a moth.

Next to the wings, it is the mouths of insects that most often indicate their relations, and here we find a strange sequence of evolutionary change. The mandibles, which are the main jaws and standard equipment for insects eating solid food, have vanished from all but a very few of the most primitive of moths, and hence an invalid diet is the rule, fluid food through a pipe. Insects have devised several ways of making a pipe out of the three pairs of limbs which normally surround their mouths, and the simplest of these is that worked out by the moths. The two maxillae, one on either side, are lengthened and somewhat hollowed out on the inner sides that face each other; these are then held together with a series of structures collectively resembling a zipper to form a single, central tube. The remaining parts of the limbs are reduced to the simplest terms. This tube, when not in use, is coiled backwards in a spiral under the head. When required it is straightened out, stuck into some exposed fluid like a drinking straw, and suction is applied. I have never seen a moth or butterfly with its straw unzipped of its own free will, but this can readily be accomplished by inserting the tip of a pin between the bases of the two half tubes, where they diverge toward either side of the head, and moving it outwards like the slide of a zipper. This, naturally, causes the owner some embarrasment, but apparently no permanent inconvenience.

All insects with tubular sucking mouthparts other than Lepidoptera have a double tube; one channel conveys the saliva outwards into the food, whereby solid components of it may be liquified, the other conveys the products inwards. More simply, they spit down one pipe and they slurp up the other (ch. 11). The moths have but a single channel, and much better manners.

The moths and butterflies are thus committed to a very limited diet; they can take no solid food, and they cannot puncture plant or animal and take sap or blood. Their diet is almost exclusively the nectar of flowers, a fairly simple solution of sugars. But almost any flower that produces it can be tapped by at least some species of moth or butterfly; these insects can often manipulate the tube into the innermost recesses of a floral nectary while they are on the wing.

The butterflies and moths have no interest in pollen, and possess neither jaws nor gizzard to grind it up nor enzymes to digest it (ch. 14). Now just as a drinking straw enables a man to keep his beard out of a milk-shake, so the long tongue of the moth, uncoiled from below her head, permits her to keep her hairy body out of the jungle of stamens with their profusion of pollen. Of those plants which have set their caps at Lepidoptera, only those with flowers which have forced them, despite their long tongues, to pass the pollen bearing anthers have been able to survive; that is, those which have evolved nectaries withdrawn in a tubular corolla. On the other hand the moths with longer tongues have also been favoured for survival since they can get more nectar for less work, and thus have their good times, including mating and laying eggs, more successfully. We have flowers today with tubular corollas as much as 12 inches deep, and, as Wallace predicted before they were known, moths with tongues to match. There must be a limit to this; when further lengthening of tongue or corolla becomes more of a hazard than a help, some other means of fertilization must be found: love will find the way?

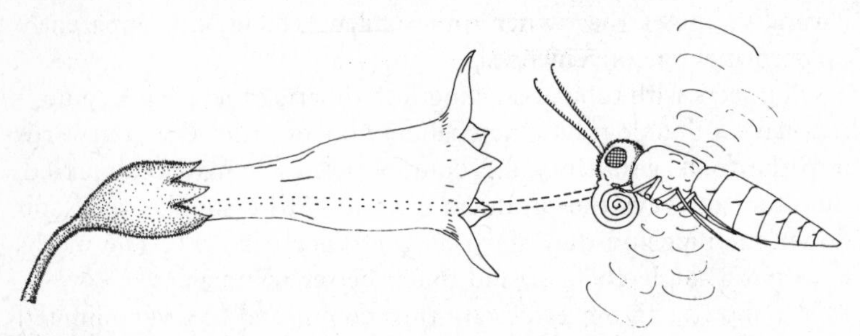

moths with tongues to match

But even among the moths, although they cannot feed on pollen directly, there is at least one that can make use of it. The yucca moth, badly off like most moths for digestive enzymes, collects the pollen of the yucca flowers, not for use as food but with apparent intent to fertilize them. For the moth lays her eggs in the pods of the flowers, where the caterpillars would starve if the seeds did not develop. She seems to fertilize the flowers deliberately, climbing down the stigma and placing her prepared ball of pollen firmly on the end of it. Of course if the caterpillars eat all the seeds there will be no plants for later generations, so that only a modest number of eggs may be laid. How does the moth know when to stop? We don't know; maybe the yucca tells her.

But if nectar is only sugar, what about fats and proteins? These are the responsibility of the caterpillar; the imported cabbage worm for the cabbage white butterfly, the woolly bear for the tiger moth, the cutworm for the miller: each youngster must lay in stocks of fat and protein to last from the day it pupates to the day it dies, not forgetting eggs for the next generation. No wonder our caterpillar ate so much cabbage, and no wonder nearly all caterpillars need stumpy little extra legs along the abdomen, to support these reserves of food and ensure that the larder tail can keep up with the gluttonous and speedy front end. There are many moths unable to feed at all; for them all the nourishment for adult life must be acquired by the caterpillar.

Nobody quite knows why, but there is one other item of diet for which butterflies especially will unroll their built in drinking straws, and this is common salt. There are many reports of butterflies landing on the sea or on saline lakes and apparently drinking; they appear to settle on perspiring mammals with the same objective. I recall on a long hot hike in Labrador removing my boots at a stop for lunch, putting my feet up on a rock, and shutting my eyes for brief relaxation. On opening them again I was alarmed to find that my feet had turned blue; I twitched my toes gingerly, half expecting them to drop off, but they took off – a dozen or so blue butterflies.

The transformation of a caterpillar into a butterfly, through the preparatory inactivity of the chrysalis, has stirred men to wonder since men first came into being. The knowledge which has recently been acquired of the nervous and hormonal mechanisms which control the process does nothing to diminish our wonderment at it. Few happenings can do more to restore our faith in life; and there are numberless variations on it. The caterpillars of most moths transform to the chrysalis inside a prepared chamber or a cocoon. This chamber may be formed in the soil, particles of which are consolidated into a wall with secretions from a pair of enormously developed salivary glands; it may be a pre-existing cavity in a plant, modified for the purpose; most commonly it is a silken bag spun from the salivary glands. The caterpillar uses its mandibles in forming the cocoon, but the moth has no mandibles and so has to get out of it without them. Although it has had no previous experience in this situation, the caterpillar seems aware of the problem that will confront it after it has become a moth and usually prepares in advance – the last task its mandibles will perform – a trap door or some other open sesame for its future convenience. The butterflies have solved this problem in a different way, a way prepared for them perhaps by their unpleasant taste. The cocoon is progressively reduced in the more specialized forms, firstly to the silk girdle and button we saw in the cabbage white butterfly, and finally to just the button of silk from which the chrysalis, fully exposed, hangs head downwards. It is the colour – bronze, silver, or gold – of many of the exposed butterfly chrysalids that has earned them all this name; a brazen challenge to would-be predators.

In such a colourful group of insects it is not surprising to find most types of animal colouration represented. Caterpillars living in the open are commonly countershaded, that is they are darker above than below, which offsets the greater illumination from sun and sky above and blends them into their backgrounds. Others may show, like some butterflies, disruptive colouration, the outline of the body or wings being broken up by a bold pattern of oblique stripes. Still others show the warning colouration that goes with stings or bad tastes. This is distinctive and conspicuous, commonly a clear banding of black and orange, yellow, or red; it is of no avail to be poisonous if nobody can recognize you.

Then of course there is mimicry of various kinds (p. 52). You don't have to be poisonous at all if you can manage to look like somebody who is, and if you can manage to resemble your background you may not be seen at all. A great many moths have wing patterns matching the bark of a particular kind of tree and always rest on this kind in the daytime. Such patterns are usually directional, so that the moths must be correctly oriented; they can sometimes be seen, as day dawns, settling down on the trunks of the trees and shuffling around to the correct angle. If you look like a fresh green leaf you may simply be eaten by a herbivore instead of a carnivore; so it is better to look like a dead leaf, or one partially eaten already or disfigured with fungus spots. Many butterflies and moths are so coloured and patterned. And finally there is flash colouration, the sudden revelation of brilliant eye-spots or red and black bands on the hind wings, usually effected by moving the front wings. This apparently deters many a would be predator; by the time the predator has recovered from his surprise, the intended victim has again vanished into its background, matched by the front wings.

The silken fibre of the cocoon of several species of moths has properties which have never been fully imitated and has been an article of commerce for some 4,000 years. The most important species is the mulberry silkworm, *Bombyx mori*, which feeds naturally on the leaves of the mulberry but which will also do quite well on lettuce. The mulberry silkworm is believed to exist now only under domestication. The secret of using this fibre depends initially on finding the end to start unwinding. It is reputed to have been discovered accidentally by the Chinese empress Si-Ling nearly four thousand years ago. In China it is called, in her honour, *si*, from which doubtless the word silk is derived. The production of this silk spread to Japan and India quite early but remained an oriental monopoly until the sixth century, when a series of happy accidents and daredevil exploits led to its introduction to Europe and elsewhere. The glands which secrete the silk, salivary glands again, are collectively ten times as long as the caterpillar, winding back and forth in the abdomen. They produce over two miles of fibre, of which rather less than half is usable, but it takes 25 hundred cocoons to yield a pound of silk. As a bonus to all this, when the fibre has been reeled off the chrysalids remain inside. These are the po-gaung-gyaw of Burmese markets; of course many po-guang-gyaw never reach the market, but go as delicious morsels to reward the reelers. Surgical thread and leaders for fishing lines are made artificially from the glands themselves. And as a final by-product Louis Pasteur in the eighteen sixties gave us the germ theory of disease, in part as a result of his studies of a disease of silkworms.

The restriction of the adult diet of moths and butterflies to sugars and salt, though it may restrict somewhat their reproductive activities, does nothing to inhibit their movement. Fuel for the migratory flights which are a characteristic feature of the lives of many butterflies and some moths comes either from nectar or from fat stored by the caterpillars. One of the widest ranging of all insects, a *Vanessa* butterfly, occurs on all continents but South America, and it may have been this species that gave rise to one of the strangest tales a sailor ever brought back from the sea: Butterflies Sink Ship – so ran the headline. The *S.S. Adler*, also spelt *Alder*, was converted into a hulk in 1910 and struck off Lloyd's register in 1911, presumably as unseaworthy, but she continued to sail. Her owners, apparently determined to get the last penny out of her, must have overloaded her creaking hull. In 1911 in the Persian Gulf a vast swarm of butterflies homed on her, change course as she might. This was the last straw that tipped the scales in favour of Neptune; the crew were just able to comply with an order to abandon ship before she sank in that silky sea. Unbelievable? Listen: in 1911 there was in Texas a migration of snout butterflies estimated to have weighed 2500 tons. There are many reasons why butterflies, their food reserves exhausted, might try to settle on an already half sunk ship. One reason, maybe they just wanted some salt.

11

Bloody Diet

WHILE the layman may refer to almost any winged insect as a fly, to the entomologist a fly means an insect near to the acme of physical perfection for flight, one of the 'true' or two-winged flies. It seems strange that this specialization for flight should again, as in the beetles (ch. 9), involve a reduction in the number of wings from the normal four of most insects to two. The second pair, however, is not lost but changed into drumstick-like organs which vibrate as gyro-stabilizers behind the true wings. These organs, if I judge aright, have played a major role in the success of this abounding group of insects. Outside of the dragonflies few insects really make use of their two pairs of wings separately. These stabilizers give flies superior control in flight and permit them such intriguing performances as the famous barrel-roll ceiling landing, hovering, and perhaps even upside-down flight.

The single pair of a fly's wings is so superb that more would be superfluous. They need superb muscles to operate them, and superb muscles need a big thoracic box to house them. The middle segment of the thorax in this group of insects has progressively incorporated one of the plates properly belonging to the legs into the wall itself in building this box. It is this swollen middle segment, wedged in between the other two parts of the thorax, which gives the flies their characteristic hump-backed appearance. No dowager's hump this, but a solid wedge of muscle.

If you look for the antennae of a house fly you may be hard put to find them; they, too, are specialized for flight, peculiar flat structures hanging down in front of the face, and they serve especially well as air speed indicators (ch. 6). In comparison, primitive flies like daddy-long-legs and mosquitoes have the obvious feelers of most other insects. The flies have pulled in their horns along their path of specialization; but what they have done with their mouths is something else again, for they have pulled them in and pushed them out in a series of facial gymnastics unrivalled in the animal kingdom.

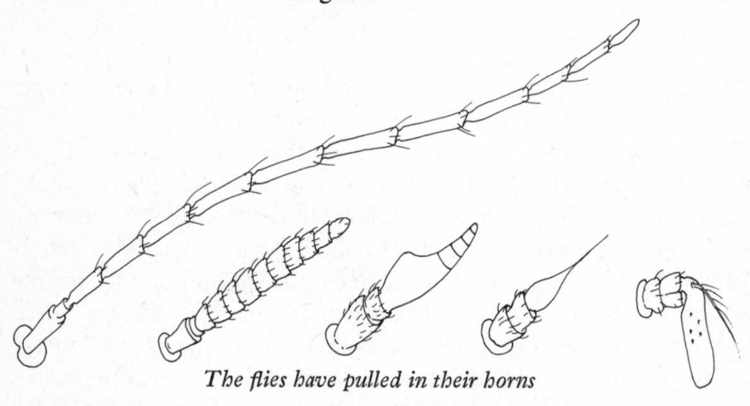

The flies have pulled in their horns

Almost since they were first thought of, the flies have had something of an interest in blood; today, this is for the most part an interest in the warm blood of birds and mammals, but it cannot have been so when it first arose, for at that time all blood was cold. And it is not, like that of lice and bed bugs, an overriding interest in blood to the exclusion of everything else. Originally it seems, only the female of the species had this blood-lust, and she only at that time of life when the urgent call for proteins for the development of eggs could not be satisfied by her normal diet of nectar. At this time her food must be sanguine as well as sapid. But there are many groups in this large order of insects which have never had any interest in blood, warm or cold, plain or coloured.

The most familiar blood-thirsty flies and the most primitive are the mosquitoes. Somewhat related to them are three other primitive groups: the punkies or no-see-ums, the blackflies, and the horse flies and deerflies, in order of increasing size. We may appropriately refer to these collectively as the other three musketeers, since mosquito and musket are words of common origin, an allusion to the miniature musket-like projection from the head of the insect. Among these four groups only the female feeds on blood; she is more deadly than the male. Some species can fire from these projecting mouthparts, shots no less deadly than musket-balls.

the miniature musket-like projection

All four groups have certain things in common. The larvae develop in water or at least in very wet environments. This in part explains their abundance in the arctic and subarctic with its vast areas of pools, sloughs, swamps and streams, which in turn are explained by the underlying permafrost. Adult male and female flies usually feed on the nectar of flowers, and again the tundra is most provident, but the females of some species in each group may also feed on the blood of other animals – almost any kind from other insects to man. The females have smaller eyes than the males, partly because they need more space between the eyes for the attachment of the rather specialized muscles which they use to suck blood.

Most species in these four groups exhibit interesting patterns of flight behaviour associated with mating. The males form dense dancing swarms, above conspicuous trees, fence posts or light patches of ground, usually at about sunrise or sundown. There are sometimes so many of these swarms that they look like smoke, and the forest appears to be on fire. Swarms may also form over the white lines painted on highways, a swarm over each dot where the line is broken, continuous where it is solid; do not pass when the continuous swarm is in your lane. If all that blood-sucking insects did was to abstract their small toll and pass on,

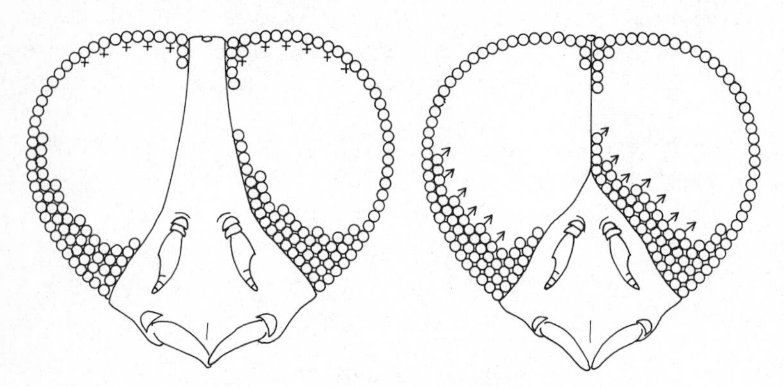

females . . . need more space between the eyes

man could perhaps smile at them, at least in small numbers. But often they take and give from host to host, be it man or other animal, some parasite foreign to both fly and host. Unseen, and unknown a hundred years ago, disease causing viruses, protozoa, and microworms have evolved along with blood-sucking flies and their hosts and use this method of self perpetuation and passage from host to unwilling host. Let us look more closely at the individual groups.

First the mosquitoes. Of the 2500 different species of mosquitoes known, only about 30 occur in northern regions. But there are plenty of them. Most of them lay their eggs on damp ground in depressions which are filled with snow-water in the spring so that the larvae, familiar to most people as wrigglers, develop in the still water of small pools. The pupae, unlike those of most insects, can be very active, and these two stages are completed in about three weeks to give rise to the adults. Some of our mosquitoes when viewed under a microscope are seen to be most attractive animals, clothed in golden brown, black, and silvery scales, some with large deep green or blue eyes. No male mosquitoes feed on blood, and there are many species in which the female doesn't either. The larvae of some of these species are predatory and eat, among other things, the larvae of some of the blood-feeding species. Although the damnable habits of some mosquitoes are expressed even in their latin names: *vexans*, *excrucians*, we cannot condemn them all out of hand. All species have a long slender beak-like proboscis projecting below the head which distinguishes the mosquitoes from their close relatives, the midges. They are the most ubiquitous of the northern biting flies and bite both by day and by night, even at temperatures close to freezing.

In lower latitudes many species, including those which transmit malaria, lay their eggs on the surface of water, some with a wee float on either side to keep them there, others glued together in rafts kept afloat by the entrapped air. Development is more rapid at the higher temperatures and generation may succeed generation continuously. Tropical species usually bite less obtrusively than those of high latitudes, but this advantage is outweighed many times by the many diseases they transmit. Usually species are more numerous in the tropics, but individuals less so.

The no-see-ums are the smallest of the biting flies, so tiny indeed that biting is the only obvious thing about them. They are the least well known, and it is only in the last few years that they have received much serious study. Their habits are very varied and only a few species feed on the blood of man. These are only abundant enough to be troublesome in rather scattered localities and at restricted times. They are so small that it is almost impossible to protect oneself from them by nets or screens, and they seem to bite more readily when they have something to push against: a hat band or a shirt cuff. Their larvae develop in various wet situations, usually water heavily contaminated with organic matter or mud. Their bites are extremely irritating, so much so that the enormous numbers produced in some peat bogs in Scotland have given rise to the belief (not held by Scots) that in cooperation with the kilt they were responsible for the development of the highland fling.

Next, the blackflies, which are also referred to a buffalo gnats in allusion to their extreme hump-backed appearance or as white-sox because of the silvery white patches which many species sport on their front legs. These are much less studied than the mosquitoes, but over a hundred species are known in North America, most of them described in the last 20 years. Why black? I don't know. Certainly many flies are blacker. Some blackflies are gloriously spangled with golden hairs and scales; perhaps this adjective is a reference to their habits, explicitly expressed in such specific names as *damnosum.* Their habits are quite varied, but the larvae and pupae of nearly all species are to be found only in running water, although this may be anything from a sluggish ditch to a mountain torrent. Some drop their eggs at random when in flight over rivers, others lay them in groups on vegetation floating at the surface, still others climb down well below the surface on stones. The larvae anchor themselves by means of tiny hooks at the end of the body to small silk pads spun on the surface of stones or vegetation in the water. The pupae are formed inside silken bags of varied fancy designs spun by the maturing larvae.

The adult females of many species of blackfly feed on the blood of birds, but relatively few attack man. They do not feed at night and the actual process of feeding is rarely felt, but the bites are more severe than those of mosquitoes; they may itch for a week or more and a hundred or two may send the victim to bed. They also have the habit of crawling inside the clothing to bite instead of biting through it like a mosquito. This they have to do because their beaks are much shorter. For routine daily activities and for their phenomenal long range flights, perhaps up to 200 miles non-stop, males and females alike emulate the mosquitoes and indulge only in the nectar of flowers. Blackflies may be terrifyingly abundant; although individually no larger than the heads of two pins, there are places in Canada where at times I have been able to collect a quart of blackflies in ten minutes. Abundance of running water is one thing that makes for abundant blackflies. Interference with their natural enemies, such as fish, may be another. Fishermen may sometimes be responsible for the too many blackflies which they complain of; and the control they sometimes ask for may also control their fish populations.

From a malaria-like disease which kills ducks in Canada to the river blindness, caused by a parasitic worm, which afflicts up to 10 per cent of the population in some tropical American and African villages, a blackfly is the villain of the piece. The protozoan in the duck and the worm in man are both delivered in the bites of blackflies. As if this were not enough, the secretions which blackflies must pass into their hosts as part payment for the blood they take may cause sickness and death. Thousands of beef cattle died from blackfly attack in the Danube valley in the nineteen-twenties perhaps because the post-war reaction against austerity led to over-fishing of sturgeon for caviar; it seems we cannot have our steaks as well as our hors d'oeuvres. Perhaps after all, black is an appropriate adjective for these tiny biting bundles of wing muscle.

The horseflies and deerflies are represented by some 300 species in North America, and earn their names from their preference for feeding on the blood of large mammals. They are also known as bulldogs for their reluctance to let go, and greenheads because of the predominance of this colour in the eyes, which cover the greater part of the head. They are given other unprintable names, too, because their feeding technique is rather clumsy and consequently painful. They do not seem to have learnt that man now walks on his hind legs only and has hands to slap with; those that attempt to feed on human blood rarely live to profit by it. They are big, husky, noisy flies, the comics of the biting-fly quartet. Their spindle-shaped larvae are to be found in waterlogged soil and organic debris in swamps and around the margins of lakes, where they drop from large black egg masses laid on over-hanging vegetation or fence posts. Some apparently eat only organic debris, while others prey on snails, worms, other insect larvae, and sometimes each other.

Only distantly related to these four primitive groups are other bloodthirsty flies, the tse-tse flies and the louse flies, for example, which are highly specialized. In these the males, like Adam, have succumbed to the temptation of the female and also indulge in blood. Here we find space between the eyes for the attachment of sucking muscles in both sexes.

Somewhere along the line, the needle- or knife-like mandibles which all the primitive groups use to gain access to blood proved a handicap to a section of the flies which developed an interest in feeding as the housefly does (p. 129), and they were lost. When the precursors of the tse-tse flies developed a new interest in this vivid food they had to evolve a new mechanism to get at it, a group of rasp-like teeth on the end of the beak, an effective if painful substitute for mandibles.

Now almost confined to tropical Africa, and somewhat symbolic of that area, the tse-tse flies have given many people pronunciation problems. These can be side-stepped by using the flies' latin generic name *Glossina*, the ones with feminine tongues, or solved by recalling Ogden Nash's verse:

> *A* Glossina morsitans *bit rich Aunt Betsy.*
> *Tsk tsk, tsetse.*
>
> (*Glossina morsitans*, or, the Tsetse)

And had Aunt Betsy subsequently died of sleeping sickness it should occasion no surprise, for these are the insects that carry this disease and its parallel in domestic animals, which have contributed much of the darkness to darkest Africa. Had Betsy also willed her riches to a foundation for research on these insects, the money would have been well spent.

The louse flies have gone a stage further along the road of

dependence on their hosts, and in doing so have acquired the flatness and texture of lice. Some have even sacrified their wings, or lose them after they have found a host. Louse flies are associated with many species of birds and mammals, but none specifically with man.

While millions of square miles of both Old and New World arctic are dominated by one or more of the four primitive groups of blood-sucking flies for most of the period when winter relents, we may take some comfort in the thought that few of these species carry human disease. It is cold comfort, since populations may be so dense that an unprotected man would lose half of his blood, with fatal results, in an hour and three quarters. This of course takes no account of the toxins exchanged for the blood. Sleigh dogs, still essential to life in many northern areas, at the height of fly time must dig holes in the ground in which to crouch for protection, and their owners anoint them and themselves – with potent mixtures of tar, balsam gum, and lard. Caribou migrate into the wind.

We can kill enormous numbers of these flies by spraying insecticides from aircraft and in so doing carve out for ourselves small havens, in time and space, among the vast northern ocean of bloodthirstiness. However, ten square miles among all the millions may cost us $5000 for a week and other things besides. We may think we would shed no tears if the mosquito *Aedes excrucians* followed the passenger pigeon to extinction, but nature is not that simple. The knowledge required to design insecticides that will kill particular insects and leave other animals unharmed is still a long way from our understanding. And if our chemical knowledge is deficient, our biological knowledge is worse. There are but few among the many hundred species of northern bloodsucking flies that we know enough about to maintain them in continuous culture in the laboratory. It is inherently unwise to destroy what we cannot recreate. Who is to say that any one of these insects may not one day fill a need, if not on this planet perhaps on another?

What then should we do about this insect blood lust? Obviously we must study it. The knowledge that study brings is itself a potent weapon. We dread what we do not understand. The fear of what insects might do is more troublesome than the knowledge of what they can do. In the meantime, we have other approaches; we can protect ourselves efficiently as a result of quite modest empirical researches into chemical repellents, protective clothing, and insect behaviour. Repellents offer the great attraction that, instead of selecting for survival those insects which can defeat our attack, as insecticides inevitably do, they select those which prefer the blood of other animals or can lay eggs without blood at all. This approach might even mean, in the fullness of geological time, that we could dispense with our repellents.

Research into the behaviour of man when subjected to intense biting fly attack may also contribute to a solution. We cannot expect to take over millions of square miles of territory occupied by myriads of animals of other species, which are fully adapted to this territory, without undergoing some adaptation ourselves. Minor adjustments in our habits and way of life will mitigate the painfulness of the process of taking over. If you visit the north in fly time, wear light coloured, loose fitting clothing of open weave but with a string vest or other bulky garment underneath to prevent the beak of a mosquito from reaching your skin. Neck and cuff openings of shirts should have zippers and should fit closely. Carry in your hip pocket a small unbreakable bottle of repellent. To complete your kit take along your best long-wearing philosophy, and a few vials of insect preservative so that if you run across any interesting looking specimens you can bring some back; for we still have a lot to learn about the fine mosquitoes bred in the north country.

In the tropics the story is a less happy one; here we encounter the specialized groups of flies as well as the primitive ones, and each group is represented by many more species than those found in temperate or arctic regions, among them those which convey the parasites causing our most important tropical diseases. In our attempts to control these diseases we have for half a century underestimated our adversaries. The adaptations of both the insects and the parasites we share with them have clearly demonstrated that neither insecticides nor drugs nor both will accomplish what was earlier expected of them. Against the recession of malaria must be set the advance of filariasis.

As in the Arctic, we need research, we need to know much more about these insects; but a greater need in the tropics is the education of the greater human populations to the facts about these insects, for they must apply what we already know. The importance of insect-borne diseases in the tropics is largely due to the density of human populations there. As this density spreads to higher latitudes, where insect densities are so much greater, we should expect new adaptations on the part of both parasites and insects. The processes of adaptation of a parasite to a new host are apt to be painful to both parties. The problems ahead of us as these things happen may be of a different order of magnitude from the unsolved problems of the tropics. They are biological, not chemical, problems.

We can protect ourselves efficiently

12

Lord of the Dunghill

THE great majority of bees and flies are strikingly different from each other. Nobody is likely, for instance, to mistake a housefly for a honey bee; but there are bees and flies which, superficially at any rate, are remarkably similar. How is one to distinguish these? Bees have been defined as insects which are sweet at one end and hot at the other. Many flies feed on nectar and other sweet materials and so may also be said to be sweet at one end, but there is no fly which carries a sting in its tail. Any stinging sensation which is received from a fly is administered not by the tail but by the mouthparts, a collection of appendages assuming a variety of forms reminiscent of cutlery, which surround the mouth at the front or lower side of the head.

The most fundamental difference between the bees and the flies, however, is in the wings. Bees have two pairs of wings, a larger pair in front and a smaller pair behind. The smaller pair is normally hooked onto the trailing edge of the larger pair, so that the two may appear as a single wing. They can, however, always be readily unhooked. The name of the order, Hymenoptera, comes from that of the Greek god of marriage, or getting hooked, Hymen. But it is much easier to unhook a bee's hind wings than to get a divorce. No fly has more than a single pair of wings, the hind wings being reduced to balancing organs (p. 109). Aristotle knew of these differences when he wrote: "Four winged insects have the sting in the tail, and the two winged ones . . . have the sting in the front of the head." This is not, however, quite so simple as it sounds, since flies which resemble bees may go to the extreme of having the front half of each wing of a different colour from the rear half, so that the wing appears made up of two parts.

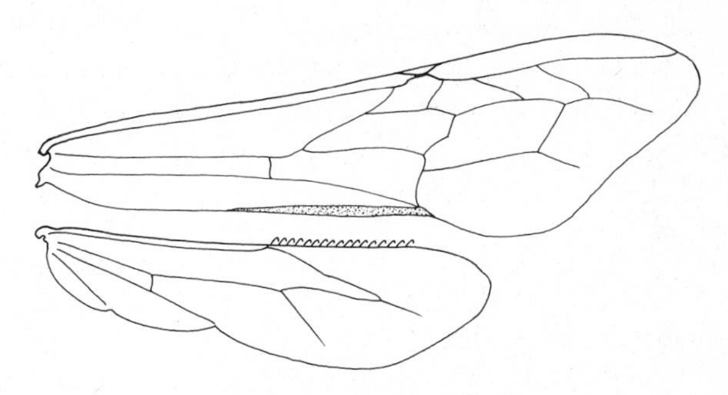

easier . . . than to get a divorce

Confusion between bees and flies gave rise to the bugonia myth; the word bugonia comes from the Greek and means ox-progeny. The essence of this belief is that the honey bee, in addition to its normal method of propagation in the hive, could be spontaneously generated in the form of a swarm from the putrefying carcass of an ox. Certain rather precise conditions were stipulated for the slaughter and the putrefaction of the ox. Similar beliefs have been held with regard to the generation of certain other bee-like insects from the carcasses of animals, especially wasps from the horse and hornets from the mule.

These beliefs appear to have originated in Egypt where, in the time of the Pharaohs, both the bull and the bee were deified. It is interesting to notice that when Linnaeus gave the honey bee its Latin name, he chose for the first part of this the name of the Egyptian bull god, *Apis*. The subject found its way into the Bible where, in Chapter 14 of the Book of Judges, Samson, having killed a lion on the way through the vineyards of Timnath to fetch his bride, "Went down and talked with the woman; and she pleased Samson well. And after a while, he returned to take her and he turned aside to see the carcass of the lion; and behold there was a swarm of bees in the mouth of the lion, and honey; and he took it into his hands, and went on, eating as he went." In Greek and Roman literature many writers refer to this question, each giving his own version of the elaborate instructions for the slaughter of the ox and for how the carcass should be allowed to decay. One of the best known accounts is given by Virgil in the Georgics.

Most of the recipes run something as follows: the animal must be carefully chosen in the spring, when the sun is in the sign of the bull, and must be killed by clubbing without shedding any blood. The body openings are to be closed with fine linen impregnated with pitch, presumably so that the vitality will remain inside for the bees. Putrefaction is to take place in an elaborately constructed house which is kept closed for three weeks and then opened, except on the windward side, for another eleven days. Then one walks in and collects the bees. On the whole it would seem simpler to await a normal swarm from another hive.

It is possible that this strange belief originated and perhaps was given new impetus at intervals by the actual discovery of bees nesting in dried out skeletons or skulls of large animals. I do not think, however, that there is any recent record of either the honey bee or any of its three related species using such a site. Belief in the bugonia myth persisted almost unquestioned through the Middle Ages and at least until the 17th century, when observers of insects in Holland and in Italy first put forward more probable explanations of the production of insects from carcasses. It was not until 1883, however, that Osten-Sacken in Germany advanced a fully acceptable explanation of the origins of the myth, and hence finally discredited it.

Myths of this kind undoubtedly arose out of the confusion of certain flies known as hover flies or flower flies with the honey bees and wasps which they resemble. Confusion of the honey bee with the drone fly, which gets its name from its resemblance to the drone of the honey bee, must be at the root of the bugonia myth itself. The larva of this very interesting fly is known as the rat-tailed maggot on account of the long breathing tube or tail at the end of its body. This tail can be extended for a distance of some five and a half inches in order to reach the surface of the usually rather unsavoury liquid in which the maggot lives. It originally bred mainly in the pools of liquid which collect beneath decaying carcasses, but now breeds very largely in sewage or other water rich in decaying organic matter. The adult fly has a very close superficial resemblance to a honey bee which is heightened by its habit of visiting and feeding on flowers.

Those who attempted to obtain a swarm of bees by the bugonia method would have had no difficulty in securing quite a collection of drone flies in about the 32 days recommended. All eternity, however, would not be long enough to obtain either a sting from the rear end or a comb of honey from the front, and had the gatherers taken the trouble to count the number of wings, they would have discovered that Aristotle could have told them the difference.

It is usually stated that insects such as the drone fly have been largely left alone by their enemies and predators, chiefly birds, being mistaken by them for bees. Their relatives lacking this protective resemblance have been unable to survive. This explanation is all very well, until one remembers that the drone, or male honey bee, has neither a sting nor any other unpleasant characteristic except laziness, and never has had.

Even if birds are unable to tell the difference between male and worker bees, we should by now know a fly when we see one; let us look more closely at that familiar species, the housefly.

As every Sunday school teacher knows, the problem of where Adam's sons Cain and Seth found their wives has always puzzled children and stirred the ingenuity of adults. Perhaps the most popular product of adult ingenuity is the supposition that Adam either married or had an illicit union with an Assyrian goddess named Lilith. The human offspring of this union included among their number the wives of Cain and Seth. Lilith apparently was a beautiful blonde, perhaps Scandinavian, and she flew well. When ultimately Adam's reactionary insistence on obedience became intolerable to her, she flew away leaving the field clear for Eve, who was as subservient as a rib.

Lilith meanwhile found herself a new husband, a Phoenician lord, Samael, with the sub-title Beelzebul meaning in Phoenician lord of the mountain. But the Hebrews, who could hardly be expected to look with favour on the new consort of their primary mother, apparently translated this contemptuously as lord of the dunghill. In this new union Lilith, it is supposed, mothered a brood of flies and also the Succubae, devils in human form, but please note that they were female devils. It is not clear whether the brood of flies or the contemptuous title for the father came first, but a connection either way is possible. In the Old Testament, the name Baalzebub means lord of the flies, -zebub coming again from the Phoenician and meaning flies of different kinds in different contexts. This has converged with the New Testament version Beelzebul, so that both are used to refer to the prince of devils.

The original flies, then, were the offspring of an illicit union between Adam's first wife, Lilith, and Samael, the prince of devils or chief of the fallen angels. Lilith herself may have been synonymous with Nin-lil, the Babylonian goddess of fertility, and certainly no more appropriate original parent for the housefly could be sought. Nin-lil, in common with Lilith and many other goddesses of this period, had the ability to fly and indeed traveled considerable distances. Perhaps this contributed to the remarkable following she had in Europe during the seventh century. And the same root has given rise, rather incongruously, to another familiar word, "lilac" a plant native to Assyria, and also to the girl's name Leila. Legend also forecast that the brood of flies arising from this original illicit union would fill the earth in order to corrupt the human race, but would be annihilated at the end of time.

You might have supposed that such a humble insect as the housefly had no history, but clearly you would have been wrong, for this is a most colourful history. And if your familiarity with this insect has bred contempt, much as a dunghill breeds flies, you have been wrong again, for there is much to admire in the housefly.

Should you, however, believe in evolution, you may perhaps question the truth of some of these aspects of the history of the housefly, colourful though they be. You may prefer to look upon this insect as having developed from a common ancestor with other flies and with the butterflies, moths, caddis flies, and fleas in a rather small and insignificant order of insects represented in North America by some strange flightless species which crawl around on the snow. These are the Mecoptera, the scorpion flies, which in many features resemble the two-winged flies. But there were no men, no flying women at this time to be preserved in legend and mythology, and the bonelessness of insects leaves us with an indifferent record in the rocks.

Whichever story of the early history of the housefly you prefer, the recent history is factual and impressive enough for anybody. The Latin name, *Musca domestica*, given this insect by Linnaeus, simply means the domestic flying insect and reflects correctly the close association which the housefly has had with man from the days of man's earliest history. Relatives of the housefly have been found in Egyptian tombs along with the mummies of the Pharaohs.

Until a half a century ago the normal breeding site for houseflies seems to have been horse droppings. When the horse was man's principal transportation as well as the provider of power for agriculture, the housefly had things all its own way. Now it is interesting to note that no less than 700 houseflies can be bred in one pound of horse dung. As those of you who are familiar with horses will be well aware, a well fed horse produces something like 45 pounds of dung in a day. A simple computation on this shows that something like thirty thousand flies are the equivalent of one horse in terms of its daily production of dung. It may be supposed, then, that the striking drop in the horse population over the last half century, as a result of its replacement by bicycles, cars, trains, and aircraft for transportation, and by tractors for agricultural power, would have led to the disappearance or at least a comparable drop in the population of the housefly. If we equate one tractor with about 30 to 40 horses, it is easy to see that each and every tractor in service represents a potential cut in housefly production of about one million houseflies per day. Today's total population of tractors should mean no flies left. But as we all know, this is far from being so.

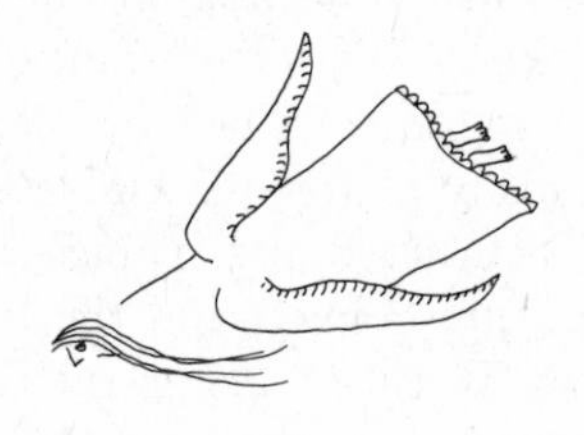

*every tractor in service
represents a . . . cut in housefly production*

The housefly is not so easily outwitted. With the reduction in numbers of horses it took to laying its eggs in privies and decaying vegetation of various kinds and managed to maintain a very healthy population. Let us take a look at the things which contribute to this success. Not only can its maggots or larvae develop in many different situations, but the adult female housefly can start to lay eggs two or three days after she emerges from the pupal stage and can proceed to lay as many as 2300 eggs in masses of perhaps a hundred at a time. These eggs hatch in very short order, giving rise to maggots which transform four to six days later into the pupal stage, from which new adults, male and female, will emerge after another three days. The life cycle can thus be completed in less than two weeks. Some further simple arithmetic shows us that one pair of houseflies in April, could, if unchecked, produce as many as 10^{20} by August.

This emergence of a housefly from the pupa, which we dismissed so briefly, deserves further comment, for it is one of the strangest events in nature. The maggots of flies transform into the pupal stage inside the skin of the last larval stage. The adult fly, then, has to make its way out through a double barrier. But the adult fly has no jaws. If you look a fly squarely between the eyes, and you may need a lens, you will notice a clear line running like an upside down U above the bases of the antennae and marking off an area including most of the front of the head between the eyes. When the fly is young this flap-like area can be hinged forward along its lower margin and thus allow an elastic and largely transparent gusset of skin, which in some species carries prominent teeth or spines, to be inflated forwards from the front of the head by blood pressure. Muscles will pull this balloon back in again, so that the process can be repeated as often as need be, until the head consolidates into its final dark and rigid form. Before this happens the balloon must be withdrawn and the flap closed; once in a while the balloon doesn't quite make it and a telltale flap is caught in the closing door to embarrass the fly for the rest of its life. It is this balloon, reminiscent of a child's best efforts with bubble-gum, which pushes off a neat circular cap at the front end of the double skin that encloses the young fly and allows it to crawl out. But this is not all.

Many flies pupate underground; they can make their way through a foot of soil by repeatedly blowing out the balloon and crawling up into the space this creates ahead of them. The backward-directed spines with which flies are adorned prevent them from slipping back. Every housefly goes through this remarkable experience of literally blowing its top as it graduates to adulthood. And incidentally, looking in through the stretched balloon one gets a fine view of the brain, nerves, muscles, and blood at work inside the living head.

Houseflies, unlike Lilith, are not great travelers, but usually stay fairly close to home as long as food and egg laying sites are available. In general it may be said, if you have a fly problem you need go no further than a city block in seeking the source of it. In general, flies are bred in the block in which they are troublesome, but they do show a slight tendency to move against the wind, encouraged by the odours it may carry.

When DDT came on the scene many thought the housefly was doomed. With the advent of modern insecticides there was, admittedly, a substantial drop in the population of houseflies for a few years, but flies have now been able to overcome many of the most toxic materials developed by man. These materials select races of flies resistant to each of them in turn, until now the usefulness of most of the poisons we have is slight. One cannot but respect an animal with such remarkable powers of adaptation.

Now, it is quite true that the housefly is something of a threat to human health. As many as four million microorganisms have been discovered on the feet and body surfaces of a single housefly. Among these four million organisms are many which cause human diseases. These diseases include the typhoid and paratyphoid fevers, infantile diarrhoea, cholera, bacillary and amoebic dysentery, anthrax, leprosy, tuberculosis, and many pathogenic protozoa including trypanosomes. But we shouldn't be too hard on the housefly; it is the unwitting and probably unwilling carrier of all of these organisms with the exception perhaps of that causing cholera. The diseases these organisms cause can get around without the housefly and are not dependent on it for their transmission. Occasionally even the eggs of another insect, *Dermatobia hominis*, the human bot fly, are found on houseflies. This ingenious animal more usually employs a mosquito to deliver its eggs to man, but is not above victimizing the unhappy fly. It presumably doesn't care to take the risk of delivery itself.

Mostly it is behaviour that makes the housefly important in disease transmission, although structure too is important; the hairy body covering does facilitate the pick-up and carriage of micro-organisms. But the most important feature perhaps is its habit of laying eggs in what are normally rather insanitary conditions, such as dunghills and privies, and feeding while doing so, and then returning to more attractive food materials such as ice cream and other dainties where it feeds itself up for the next batch of eggs. In this way it transfers microorganisms on the outside and inside of the body from the egg laying site to the feeding site. The material ingested with a meal from the dunghill will be regurgitated with saliva in order to dissolve the different food material at the table. You are probably familiar with the habit of the housefly of pilfering food from the table and even following it up to the mouth and stealing it from the very lips of the consumer. Shakespeare recognized this habit of flies in another group, the carrion flies, in *Romeo and Juliet*:

> *More honorable state, more courtship lives*
> *In carrion-flies than Romeo: they may seize*
> *On the white wonder of dear Juliet's hand,*
> *And steal immortal blessings from her lips;*
> *But Romeo may not; he is banished:*
> *Flies may do this, but I from this must fly;*

It is important to distinguish between an insect like the housefly and the carrion flies, the larvae of which are to be found in the bodies of animals, usually dead ones. The maggots which dispose of the carcasses of animals are those of carrion flies or blow flies, a different family with very different habits from the housefly. Shakespeare presents a fuller picture of carrion flies when Hamlet, replying to the King's enquiry as to the whereabouts of the slain Polonius, says:

At supper . . . Not where he eats, but where he is eaten: a certain convocation of politic worms are e'en at him. Your worm is your only emperor for diet: we fat all creatures else to fat us, and we fat ourselves for maggots: . . . A man may fish with a worm that hath eat of a king, and eat of the fish that hath fed of that worm.

But these two groups of flies have one desirable feature in common. Both of them are excellent at garbage disposal. The first group, represented by the housefly, disposes of decaying vegetation and the droppings of herbivorous animals; the second, the carrion flies, disposes of the bodies of the animals themselves. Despite the clearly undesirable features of the housefly, I think we should recognize the credit side as well as the debit. We may dislike the housefly, or be filled with revulsion at the sight of it, but we cannot but respect this animal for its adaptability, its prolific powers of reproduction, and its long and faithful association with ourselves. Clearly it appreciates us, even if we do not as yet reciprocate.

13

Gall Enough in Thy Ink

IT was a sunny afternoon nearly two thousand years ago in Chinese Turkestan near where now stands the city of Kashgar; Leng fu was awakened from a satisfying slumber under an old magnolia tree by the sudden buzz of a wasp past his upside ear. Had you been there, you would have recognized the insect as a vespid wasp resembling the familiar yellow jackets of this other time and place, twentieth century North America; evolution is a slow process. She was a female wasp and it was early in the year. She was one of a small group, among the many thousands of her colleagues of the previous summer, who was fully female and had consorted with a male. She had been more successful than most of her group in her search for a protected, thermally favoured crevice before the hard winter began. She alone had survived it. Had you watched her as Leng fu did, peering into the bright sky, you would have seen her settle on a dead and peeling branch of the old magnolia, parallel to its length, and attack its outer fibres with vigorous transverse strokes of her capable mandibles. The branch yielded a cluster of fibres to this treatment, and a close examination of it would have revealed that she had been there before. She took off moments later and returned whence she had come, to a low and sheltered branch of a lilac, from which depended a fibrous filament expanded at the lower end; and to this she added her cargo of fibres from the magnolia.

As the day drew to a close the structure hanging from the lilac branch grew and developed under her care until finally it could best be described as a small paper ball open at the lower end. And paper it was indeed, a felted mat of cellulose fibres precipitated from the salivary secretions of the wasp and dried into a thin layer. The wasp laid her first eggs next day in the paper cells inside the paper ball, and in the fullness of time she and her children built it as big as a football to house the many thousands of offspring which she raised during that summer season in the first century A.D. Inside, with infinite artistry, several tiers of hexagonal paper cells were constructed, their openings downwards. Each tier depended from that above it by slender pillars, and all depended from a single security on the branch of the lilac. And Leng fu watched her; that first day when she awoke him and on many later days; and as he watched he thought. When cold weather robbed the wasps' nest of its defenses, he robbed it of some of its outer layers and tore them apart and examined them patiently. He even chewed on the dead magnolia branch and spat out the pulp it yielded to him. He worked on it with tools and with water, dried it on rocks in the sun. He made our first paper, learning the secret from wasps which had made it for perhaps fifty million years before him.

This of course is only fantasy; history has no record of Leng fu or his wasp. But the earliest record we have of paper – as distinct from papyrus, biblos, parchment, and tablets of wax or clay – comes from the first century A.D. and from Chinese Turkestan, where Sir Aurel Stein discovered several rolls of it neatly folded. Some seven hundred years later, Arabs, in belligerent contact with Chinese, learned the secret of paper making from some of their prisoners and went into the business themselves in Samarkand. Thence the art spread to Toledo in 1150, to Italy a hundred years later, and to Germany fifty years after that. Although paper was generally available from about 800 A.D. onwards, it was made in only a few places. In England, Elizabeth the First's jeweler John Spielman (later Sir John for his pains) brought the secret from Germany and in the uneasy peace that followed the

Spanish Armada was licensed in 1589 "to make white writing paper, and to gather for the purpose all manner of linen rags, scrolls or scraps of parchment, old fishing nets, etc." It was not until 1690 that the first paper mill in America went into operation in Pennsylvania.

Early paper was made in sheets by hand and the best still is. The name Whatman is synonymous with quality in paper. But it was not long after the first James Whatman started production at Maidstone in 1747, to make his reputation with both drawing paper for the arts and filter paper for the sciences, that machines were invented which produced paper continuously in the roll. Then the trouble started. Today many of us use more paper than we do bread, and the world produces enough each year to lay a ten mile wide strip around the equator. I suspect we even out-produce the wasps. But what is paper without ink?

. . . .

Epaminondas sat under the oak and thought; a wasp, uncertain as to her future – a female wasp of course – hummed softly past his ear. His thoughts rambled on into a comfortable day dream.

This wasp was not one which you would recognize as resembling a familiar yellow jacket of today, but one that most of you would probably fail to recognize as a wasp at all. She was a small, mostly black, rather shiny insect, but two to three millimeters long, with few veins in her hairy wings, and a peculiarly shortened abdomen. Not a wasp to waken a sleeper, be he Chinaman or Greek. Neither was she a wasp to make paper, but one which, by some subtle mechanism still beyond man's comprehension, persuades a plant to grow a nest for her. A gall wasp. Perhaps, since the name wasp has the same origin as the word weave and relates to the paper making habit displayed by our Chinese vespid, our shiny black lady should forfeit the name wasp altogether; in any event, to avert confusion we shall use her classical name

Cynips, appropriately enough of Greek origin, and meaning an insect living under bark.

It was not then the Greek, but the bark of the tree under which he sat which attracted our *Cynips*, and I said that she was female of course because many species of *Cynips* appear to have found a way to dispense with males and rarely, if ever, produce them. Others, including the heroine of our story, produce them only in alternate generations: females only, sometimes wingless, in the spring; both sexes in the fall. Both generations of many species of *Cynips* show a strange faithfulness to the oaks, but the mated females in the fall may lay their eggs in the roots, and they may differ so profoundly both from their parents and their children that they have been assigned in error to different species and even to different genera. This is a strange departure from the maxim, like father like son. The galls too, in which these alternating generations are raised, may differ as much as the insects which emerge from them. But it was spring, and our *Cynips* being female sought a place to deposit her eggs.

When a *Cynips* lays an egg in the bark of an oak twig a train of events is set in motion which culminates, so far as we are concerned at the moment, in the plant's producing a growth for (if my biological readers will forgive the word) the protection and nourishment of the maggot-like young *Cynips*. This growth is a rounded swelling variously referred to as an oak apple, gall nut, or marble-gall. After many exciting events which occur within this growth, it will eventually, unless it is first seized upon by some avaricious ink-maker, yield another *Cynips* who will leave a small round hole in its surface as witness to her departure.

Epaminondas and his colleagues knew well the properties of gall-nuts which, when extracted with boiling water, yield a solution which turns an inky black on mixture with iron dissolved in acid. This product, iron gallotannate, has been the principal writing ink of commerce for over two thousand years, and the best galls for making it to this day come from the Eastern Mediterranean; Aleppo galls, Smyrna galls, and Istria galls, each with their special characteristics, are still articles of commerce. But Epaminondas knew nothing of the relationship between *Cynips* and the gall. It was left to Martin Lister, a nephew of Queen Anne's physician, to discover the insect origin of galls in the seventeenth century. Malpighi in Italy, whose name is better known to entomologists for his work with the excretory organs of insects, noted this relationship independently in his book *De Gallis* at about the same time.

It is worth noting that ink was invented several hundred years before paper when it was used on papyrus and parchment, the forerunners of this material. It was invented so much earlier that we have no real clues as to how it happened, as to what strange accident led Epaminondas' grandfather to crush and boil gall-nuts and mix the result with old iron in acid. Theophrastus wrote about gall nuts, more than 200 years before Christ. Dioscorides gave a recipe for ink about 50 A.D. The origin of the word "ink" goes back beyond gall nuts and old iron; it is derived through the French "encre," from the latin "encaustum," a term which referred to coloured clay that was burnt into tiles used in a form of writing which preceded the use of ink.

The word "gall" on the other hand has both a double origin and a double or at least a two-sided meaning. The latin name for a gall-nut was "galla," but there was an Anglo-Saxon word "gall" which meant bitterness, irritation, or offensiveness, hence also bile and gall-bladder. And of course gallic acid (chemists now call it 3,4,5, trihydroxybenzoic acid) is bitter; the irritation by *Cynips* leads to the growing of a gall on the oak and the irritation of a saddle may lead to the formation of a gall on a horse. It was an apt play on this double meaning when Shakespeare had Sir Toby Belch tell Sir Andrew to use "gall enough" in the ink with which he penned his challenge to Viola.

Other galls, produced by other plants in response to other insects, have a bitterness of gallic acid and have been used for the making of ink. Among them are some from poison ivy, which should put a real sting into a challenge! But for everyday writing, oaks and *Cynips* are the preferred combination; this is recorded for posterity in the technical name of a most favoured species of gall wasp, *Cynips gallae-tinctoriae*, the insect that lives under bark and makes ink galls. But I think these insects deserve more tangible recognition.

It would be difficult to estimate the importance of the role of ink and paper in the development of what we are pleased to call our civilizations, past and present. Cynics have said that the quickest way to stop a war would be to cut off the supply of paper; but we would still need paper on which to sign a peace treaty. Ink and paper have served our needs well for records of language and for two-dimensional expression of form for many centuries. New media may supplement them, but will not soon

replace them. They are not immune to abuse, as when memoranda replace memory and symbols replace reality. And there are real dangers in these abuses; the threats remain remote so long as the majority of men remain illiterate, but: "If all the world were paper and all the seas were ink," there would be cause for concern. Let the truth of this matter lie where it may, I would like to see some paper magnate or publishing tycoon underwrite memorial statuary to the Vespids and the *Cynips*, to these two wasps, respected yet rejected, to whom in the last analysis he at least owes so much.

14

Bees' Knees and Corsages

IN the days before bubble-gum, when candy was candy, when one school child asked another school child what it was that he was eating, the stock reply was: "Bees' knees and flies' eyebrows." Most of us who used this quaint retort had no appreciation of what was involved in a bee's knee, and still less perhaps in a fly's eyebrow. Leaving the eyebrows of the fly for the moment, let us take a closer look at the knee of a bee, an articulation even more important to our economy than that of the housemaid.

Many people are under the impression that only two or three kinds of bees exist, but there are in North America well over three hundred species. There are for example some 60 species of bumble-bees and their relatives, and over a hundred species of leaf-cutter bee. Our honey bee, more properly called a hive bee, is only one species, although there are several races; but in numbers of individuals it probably exceeds all other bees. Indeed it is the only species for which we can make an intelligent guess at the number of individuals: there are probably something like 300 thousand million honey bees in America north of Mexico at the height of the season, roughly a hundred bees for every human being in the world.

One of the features which distinguishes all bees from almost every other insect is the fact that the hairs of the body are branched, and this, as we shall see, has an important bearing on our original subject, the bee's knee.

For the moment we will consider only the knees of the honey bee, since these are both the most numerous and the most remarkable of all bees' knees. The pedant will insist that there is no joint in the leg of a bee which can strictly speaking be referred to as the knee, but for our purposes, the interesting joint is the one at the top of the first relatively long segment above the foot end, the tibiotarsal joint. Now, the bee has three pairs of these joints, each pair very different from the other two, and each pair of agricultural importance.

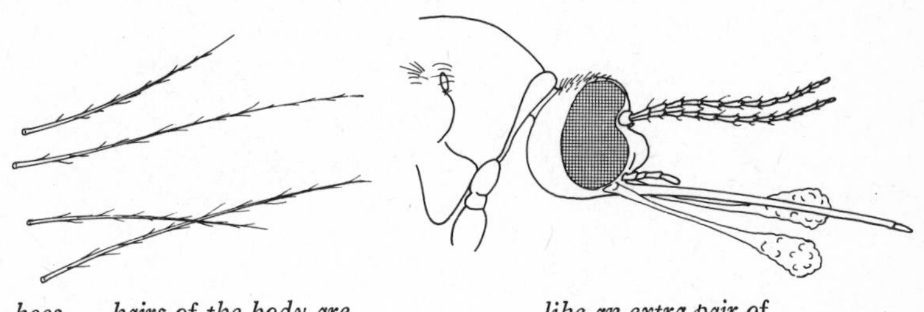

bees . . . hairs of the body are branched

like an extra pair of monstrous antennae

The links between flowers and insects are close and intricate. It is no exaggeration to say that nearly all the flowers familiar to most of us who are not botanists owe their existence to insects. And it is equally true that many of our familiar insects owe their existence to flowers. The two have evolved together through the ages, mostly it would seem in a spirit of tolerant rivalry, but occasionally with a practical joke on one another. Rarely has a development gone beyond a joke, as in the evolution of the insectivorous plants and of the cutworms.

The recognition marks of an insect-pollinated flower are showiness and scent; large colorful petals, symmetry of form, and a smell usually, but not always, agreeable to the human nose. These are the very things which we like to find in flowers and normally associate with them. Flowers with these features are almost invariably insect-pollinated; those without them are pollinated by birds or bats or by wind, rain, or some other agency. But the important parts of insect-pollinated flowers are the stamens and their product, pollen, important to both the flower and to some insect visitors, and the nectaries, producing nectar which is merely bait. It is the collection of pollen and its transfer to other flowers which makes bees' knees of agricultural importance.

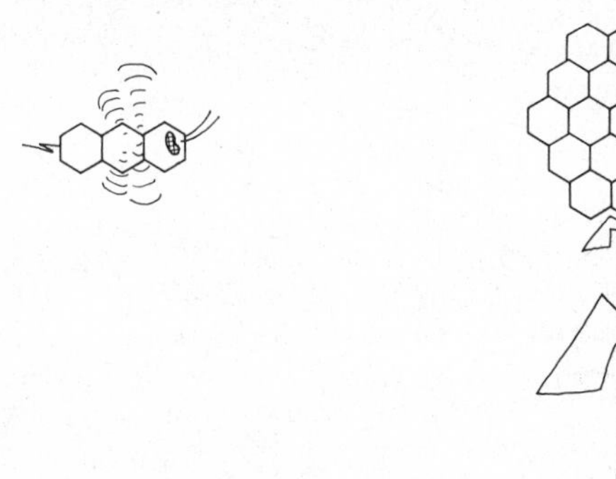

links between flowers and insects are close and intricate

Although the most important, bees are not the only insects interested in pollen, nor are entomologists the only people. Botanists talk of pollen, so to speak as their home ground; geologists hold forth as from ages past; allergy sufferers with more feeling than anybody. Entomologists speak of pollen as outsiders, almost as a garbage man might speak of what he gathers, for this is where insects come into the story of pollen. Except in rare instances (p. 104), the insects show no sign of interest in the true purpose of this potent powder. An important thing about pollen is that the different kinds can be identified, for they have characteristic structure and colour. Most people think of pollen as yellow, but it may be anything from black through green to red. This permits us, by examining a few grains collected off an insect, to make an intelligent guess at what the insect has been up to, much as a wife might draw conclusions by examining the colour of a hair from her husband's coat.

That pollen should be an important food to insects can hardly be surprising to anybody with knowledge of its chemical make up. Chemical analyses of pollen read very much like labels on containers of patent baby foods or invalid supplements: a generous proportion of protein, carbohydrates, some fats, and all the vitamins and minerals you could ask for. It is mostly as baby food that insects use it, since the high protein content permits the rapid growth of body tissues of the infant insect.

Nectar on the other hand, though bought at the same store, is an almost purely carbohydrate diet. It is a solution of simple sugars, in various proportions and concentrations up to about 75 per cent; an energy food, containing minor amounts of flavouring esters. These two items, nectar and pollen, combined in suitable proportions can meet the needs of a great many insects at any stage of their development.

When a man goes courting and takes with him a bunch of flowers, or presents his partner to a dance with a corsage, he is trading on the assumption that the object of his attentions has similar preferences in colours, design, and scent to those of insects. The relatively high success rate among suitors using this technique testifies to the validity of this assumption; and the more we learn about the senses of insects the more surprising does this seem to be. We can be more specific. Characteristically, certain types of flowers are attractive to and hence are visited and pollinated by certain types of insects; a man who takes along a bunch of our little woodland orchids is paying his lady love the doubtful compliment of likening her tastes to those of a mosquito. I would recommend, if it is the belle of the ball you are after, that you choose a flower with a tubular corolla and perhaps a flat top, one of the so-called moth or butterfly flowers such as honeysuckle or dianthus. On the other hand, for a good homemaker one could hardly do better than a bunch of clover, the preference of bees.

Although it is usually the nutritional appetites which the flower appeals to in attracting pollinators, this is not always so. In at least one example the reproductive appetite is involved. Among the most specialized insect-pollinated flowers are the orchids. Some species of the orchid genus *Ophrys* have a specific resemblance to the females of some species of bees, and come into flower only after the males of their particular bee have emerged, but before the females do so. The resemblance of the flower to the female bee is good enough to deceive the male who, in trying to mate with the flower, accomplishes its pollination. Thus is the reproductive activity of the insect used to accomplish the reproduction of the plant. What the female of such an insect has to say to him about the pollen on his coat when he finally finds her, we are alas unlikely to know. Another species, the bee orchid, also resembles a bee, but seems to have lost touch with its pollinators and is now self pollinated. In some orchids the pollen is carried as a pair of special structures known as pollinia, which have long stalks with sticky pads at the base. From a mosquito's viewpoint these are one of the unkindest inventions of the botanical world. When a mosquito visits the flowers seeking nothing more than a sip of nectar, one or perhaps both of the sticky pads become permanently stuck on its face close to the eyes, like an extra pair of monstrous antennae. No matter how one dislikes mosquitoes, one cannot but feel sorry for the unfortunate victim as one watches its frantic attempts to remove the unwelcome addition to its head on withdrawing from an orchid. Some orchids even project the pollinia at their insect victims. Even after the insects have fulfilled the purpose of the flower, visited another and transferred the pollen, there is no reprieve; they seem to be condemned to carry the badge until their dying day, which may perhaps come earlier because of this conspicuous incubus. Pollinia may also be carried by moths or bees, but for them the load does not seem inordinate.

Other groups of plants, too, inflict penalties on the insects which aid in dispersing their pollen. Among the keeled flowers of the pea family some, such as alfalfa and broom, have to be tripped to be pollinated. The organs are sometimes released from the keel with such violence that they administer a severe blow on the head to the unfortunate visitor. Bumble-bees are mostly either too stupid to avoid the blow or too robust to care. The honey bee, however, will not put up with this sort of treatment; this is why bumble-bees are better pollinators of these plants. But things must not be made too difficult or the insects will seek another approach, such as chewing directly into the nectary with their mandibles.

The greatest eaters of pollen are the bees. Examine any part of a bee you wish, and you will find some structural feature related to its interest in pollen. But the legs are most striking. Collection is an elaborate process, and to understand it fully it is best to examine the legs of a honey bee with a lens or a microscope. The bee assists the release of the pollen grains from the anthers of the flower by means of its jaws; the pollen grains then become caught up in the branched hairs all over the body of the bee, principally on the under side. At the knees of each of the first pair of legs is a notch into which an antenna of the bee will just fit. A little flap can be used to close this notch so that when the antenna is drawn through it, the pollen which is caught on it is removed and transferred to the leg. The next knee of importance is that of the hind leg. The last long segment of each of these legs is broad and flat, and carries on its inner surface a series of about ten neat combs of stiff hairs. The bee uses its tongue to moisten them with nectar and then combs out with them the pollen from the hairs of the body and the other legs. This, and the succeeding activities, are all accomplished while the bee is flying, on its way to another flower or back to the hive. At the knee itself on the hind leg projecting downwards from the upper segment, is a further comb of stout bristles, and facing upwards on the lower segment is a scoop-like projection known as the auricle. The stout comb removes the pollen from the series of combs on the lower segment of the opposite leg, and as the leg is bent the auricle forces the resulting mass of pollen up into a structure named, rather unhappily, the pollen basket. I would hate to be condemned to bring home the bacon in a basket of this nature; it is simply a hollow groove along the outside of the segment above the knee, partially closed by long curved hairs from its edge. Here the now sticky pollen accumulates as a conspicuous pellet. It can readily be seen on the outer sides of the hind legs as pollen collecting bees return to the hive or nest. The colour of these pellets is some indication of the flowers from which they have come, and a microscopic examination of them usually enables certain identification.

It is after the bee has returned to the hive with these pellets on its hind legs that the knees on the middle pair of legs come into action. Projecting from the inside of each of these joints is a long spur, which is used to prise the pellet of pollen out of its basket so that it may be stored in the cells of the hive for future feeding.

A similar but usually simpler process of pollen collection is carried out by most bees. On examination of almost any kind of bee it will be found that in addition to the branched hairs on the body, the last long segment of the hind legs is somewhat flattened, thus providing space for the combs on the inner surface. Leaf cutter bees carry their pollen on the underside of the abdomen; carpenter bees eat it, to regurgitate later. The honey bee, however, is the most specialized for pollen collection of all bees, and its legs are quite literally built for this purpose.

What, you may ask, has all this to do with the economy? As far as the bees are concerned, nothing. It is a case of plunder; the bees are out for what they can get. But as far as the plant is concerned it is quite another story; the setting of seed and fruit by a great many plants depends on the fertilization of the flower with pollen from another flower. The number of pollen grains needed for this purpose is quite small, and since most flowers produce a superabundance of pollen, it is of no concern to the plant how much the bee takes home with it, providing these few important grains are transferred to a second flower. This accident, as far as the bee is concerned, nearly always happens since bees do not normally get a full load of either pollen or nectar from a single flower or plant, and since even when they are only collecting nectar they often carry sufficient pollen on their bodies for this purpose. For a great many plants, this necessary transfer of pollen can only be made efficiently by bees or by other flower visiting insects, and for some a particular species of insect is necessary.

The honey bees' mouthparts have special features for handling pollen too, but the story doesn't stop here; between the crop and the stomach is a special valve apparently designed to permit the selective passage of nectar or pollen.

Just how important bees are to the seed grower may be illustrated by a few figures. It takes about 300 red clover flowers to give one bee load of pollen, and it takes about 10 bee loads of pollen to nourish one bee from egg to adult. To nourish a single complete colony of bees throughout the season requires some 2 million such loads weighing together between 50 and 100 lbs. To collect this enormous amount, 600 million clover flowers have to be visited, and incidentally pollinated. We can go further. If we assume that the colony produces 100 lbs. of surplus honey, then in eating 1 lb. of honey you encourage the pollination of no less than 6 million clover flowers. Ponder this as you digest this most assimilable food.

Honey bees we can manage; we can arrange to have populations of them where we need them and when we need them. Few other species, such as bumble-bees or leaf-cutters, are as yet amenable to our control, except in the sense that we "control" pest insects. Yet we depend on them. Their biology, behaviour, and relationship with their environment are absorbing studies, for we all absorb their products, direct or indirect, but we are not the only ones. Yeasts, ubiquitous microorganisms on flowers and fruits, are quick to seize upon nectar which has been insufficiently ripened, by the removal of water, into honey. The anaerobic breakdown of the sugars yields alcohol, and it is held by some that the resultant mead antedated wine as an antidote for sorrows. When produced by accident mead is potable, perhaps interesting, but not exactly exciting; produced by design it provides a fine use for honey, should we ever have a surplus of it.

INSECTS AND US

In which, against the background of numbers and of what has gone before, we take a look backwards in time in order to peer forwards at the prospects for insects, for ourselves, and for each in relation to the other.

15

And Two Khaki

IT cannot have been long after the turn of the century, when Gregor Mendel's demonstration of the ratios of the three forms in the second filial generation from a hybrid cross was rediscovered, that a limerick mnemonic for these ratios was written. The author, I believe, is unknown. Perhaps advisedly so, since his work might, even today, be banned in some places and burned in others. I hope, in including it here, I am not predisposing these pages to such a fate.

There was a young fellow named Starkey
Who had an affair with a darkey;
The result of his sins
Was quadruplets, not twins,
One white, one black, and two khaki.

Langford Reed ascribed the authorship of an inferior version of this limerick to "a well-known Brighton clergyman" but wisely did not name him. His version is unacceptable to me, firstly because his ratios are not Mendelian, and secondly because it puts the blame on the lady.

It is interesting, though incidental, that three colour groups of ants occur in roughly these same ratios. More than fifteen hundred kinds of white ants or termites have been described and perhaps nearly three times this many true ants, of which maybe a third are black or nearly so, while two-thirds may be appropriately referred to as khaki. The word khaki comes from the Hindustani for dust, which may certainly be, like our ants, any colour from yellow, through the reds, browns, and greys to almost black. Of course the relationship of Mendelian ratios to these facts is still more tenuous than their relationship – if that is the right word – to the affairs of Mr. Starkey. Indeed the relationship between white ants and true ants is barely more than an etymological one; two groups that come under the purview of the entomologist could scarcely be more widely separated. We can make this clearer by saying something about each.

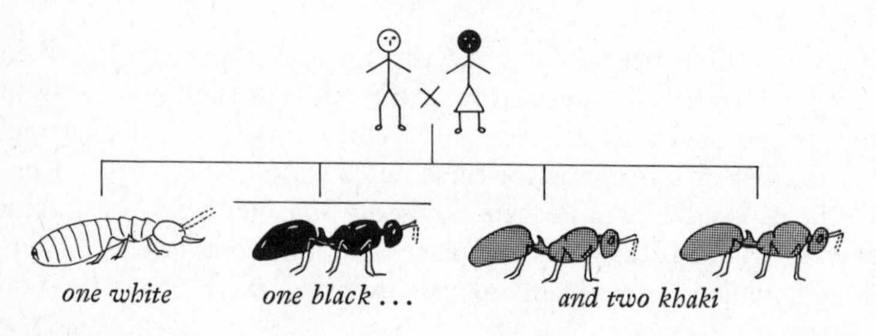
one white *one black . . .* *and two khaki*

We have seen (p. 81) that the termites or white ants are socializing cockroaches with a phenomenal appetite for wood. This relationship between cockroaches and termites is one of the clearer parts of the evolutionary story of insects. There are some cockroaches which live as family groups in rotten logs, where they feed on the wood. Like many termites, they house in their guts protozoa which digest for them this unpalatable material and thereby help to provide them with a balanced diet. They must live as family groups so that the young may acquire their pet protozoa. Most female cockroaches lay their eggs grouped together in capsules which the mother carries around in a pocket, formed by tucking the end of the abdomen in, until the eggs are ready to hatch. It is said of domestic species that if they did not do this their colleagues would eat the eggs; under crowded domestic conditions they probably would – and should. In the dark damp habitats of more normal roaches, in the tropics and sub-tropics, other egg-eating predators may have favoured this habit; or perhaps it is simply an expression of motherly affection. Anyhow, the packaged eggs of the roach may be viewed as a short step on the long road to the familial megalopolis of termites in their termitarium. Another step along this road, the loss of wings, binding the loser to the ground, has also been taken by many roaches.

Among the more old-fashioned termites we find, for their part, many echoes of the cockroach way of life. Social organization may be simple, and workers and soldiers not greatly differentiated from the reproductive forms. While no white ants are bleached beyond a very dirty white, or very light khaki, primitive species may exhibit the rich cockroach brown of most domestic roaches. Dwellers in darkness have no need of pigments; selection eliminates a superfluity as effectively as it fixes a fortuitous advantage. Up-to-date termites not only dwell in darkness, but forage and work and play in darkness too, building intricate ad hoc earthen tunnels wherever they wish to go. While most termites have flimsy wings, both pairs alike, with pre-formed break-off lines at the bases where they are removed following the mating flight, there is one conservative species which has large lobes on the trailing edges of the hind wings. These lobed hind wings are precisely similar to those of roaches and, like them, have no break-off lines. This same conservative species lays its eggs in groups, but without the cockroach's capsule.

Though typical termites – white ants – are khaki rather than white and cockroaches rather than ants, the name termite, meaning wood-worm, is at least appropriate. In the tropics and sub-tropics they play a major role in the return of the cellulose of plants to biological circulation. Without them, both the timber of trees and the paper which man digests it to, might persist for centuries; but without their protozoa and fungal colleagues they are powerless to digest cellulose and die in days. Though cellulose is their primary diet, they have a strange predilection for the proteins in vegetable tanned leather. I have known them to return paper money to biological circulation when this has been baited with a leather wallet, and to leave neat rows of nails and eyelets where boots of the uninitiated have been left under a camp bed at night. But an injustice was done when they were blamed for the disappearance of a steamroller from an army depot in India during the last war.

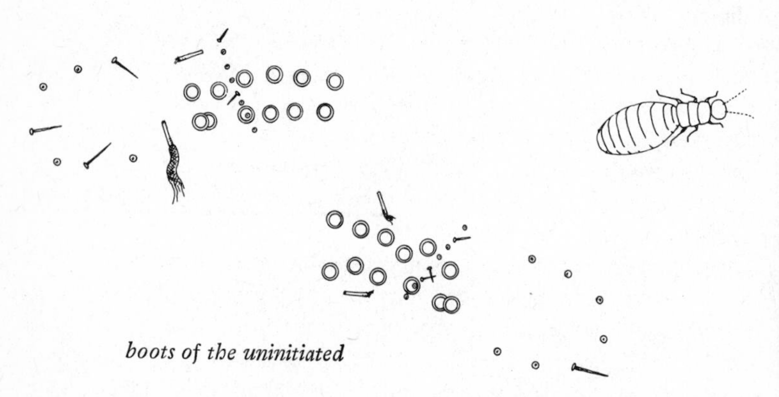

boots of the uninitiated

Special individuals for special purposes is the social policy of many insects, but none have carried it so far as the termites. The special purposes are reproduction, foraging and construction, and defence; the special individuals are royalty, workers, and soldiers; each may differ more from the others, superficially, than from other species or even from other genera. Yet each comprises male and female, though only among royalty do they function as such. And only the royalty develop functional wings; even they break them off and dispose of them as soon as dispersal and pairing have been accomplished. In no other social insect, perhaps in no other social animal, has the male been so completely integrated into society.

Within the dark dampness of termitaria up to thirty feet high, or extending many feet down into the ground, these three forms live in total numbers up to over a million, all of them the offspring of two original parents. Each form or caste is there as both male and female and in at least four growth stages, making a total of at least 24 expressions, discounting eggs, of one species. And some termitaria house, in apparent amity, more than one species. No wonder those who would classify them have, at times, created more confusion than order. Bizarre associates, strangely modified insects, other arthropods, reptiles, and even birds may live with them, parasitizing, or perhaps contributing in some still uncertain way to the social security of these welfare states. For as long as the termitarium remains intact, its inmates are secure; minor damage to the structure is defended immediately by soldiers equipped either with mandibles capable of gripping the intruder more securely than their necks grip their heads, or with squirt guns which economic entomologists might covet. Behind these defences workers repair the damage in minutes.

With this brief sketch of the termites, the white ants, in mind, we may now pass on to the black and the khaki, the true ants, for comparison. Though there are many more kinds of true ants than of termites, true ants comprise only a superfamily of the order Hymenoptera while the termites comprise a complete order, the Isoptera. The ants, like the bees, are derived from wasps, but they have gone in a different direction. Like termites they have foregone the use of wings save for dispersal and pairing, and are largely earthbound, although often, like a few termites, arboreal. Everybody who has ever sat on an ant hill knows that ants are great aggressors; they are successful too. Ants are said to outnumber most terrestrial animals, and in total weight this may be true. Ant aggression is often directed against the defensive termites to which they seem to be naturally antipathetic. In the open the issue is rarely in doubt. I feel sure that profound military lessons could be learned from closer study of the interactions between these two groups of insects.

Despite the superficial similarities between ants and termites, there are two basic differences. The termites develop directly; the young are active and in general resemble the adults except as regards wings among royalty. They contribute towards the economy of the colony. The young of ants are incompetent legless grubs, so different from the adults that they must pass through a further incompetent stage, the pupa, to accomplish the transformation. The adults must care for these stages. While among termites both sexes are found in each caste, among ants only females are modified for specialized functions of the colony, and the male's only function is maleness. Male ants develop from unfertilized eggs. What bearing, if any, these profound differences have on each other or on defensive and aggressive behaviour, remains obscure.

The impression I have so far given of ants is misleadingly simple. They are complex, as individuals and as colonies. Many primitive ants are entirely carnivorous and must migrate from one temporary nest to another to obtain the food they need. These are the driver ants, whose voracity has been widely recorded by science and embellished by fiction. More specialized ants feed increasingly on materials of plant origin; some cultivate fungi in subterranean gardens, foraging for the vegetable substrate on which to grow these; others herd aphids or scale insects which feed on the sap of plants and excrete droplets of surplus sweetness in response to appropriate stimuli from the ants. Nests may be excavated in the ground or adapted from naturally occurring cavities of almost any kind, especially the hollow parts of plants. Some species sew the leaves of trees together to form a cavity, using a silk-spinning larva as needle and thread. Such cavities are frequently divided into subcavities by curiously curvaceous lamellae fabricated of plant fibres. Within these nests the young are fed, and from them, usually at favorable season, the winged sexual forms emerge in synchrony with those from neighbouring nests. Males do not long survive this mating flight; females shed their wings and start new colonies or may return to existing ones.

The ant colony is held together by three communication systems, auditory, olfactory, and tactile. Ants produce sounds and odorous substances, and have characteristic sculpturing of the body surfaces. Their senses of hearing, smelling, and feeling are well developed. There is an old fable which links the origin of the ants with the deification of a man for his remarkable olfactory sense; a handful of earth he held when leaving for his new life above fell to the ground in the form of ants. Outside the nest, odour trails may be laid down which other ants can both follow and know which way is home. Also produced by ants are substances known as pheromones, by analogy with hormones, which control the production of the different castes as they are needed. To the armament of the termites the ants have added a sting, developed from the remnants of the egg-laying structures no longer required by the sterile female, the worker. With all this equipment it is not surprising that ants are such successful aggressors. Ogden Nash's question, though applied to the wrong sex, is pertinent:

The ant has made himself illustrious
Through constant industry industrious.
So what?
Would you be calm and placid
If you were full of formic acid?

Other insects which associate closely with ants need to be something more than bizarre; they need to be protected. In many species a skirt-like extension around the body serves this purpose, preventing ants from getting at the legs and soft under parts. Among these is a cockroach; it is hard to say what strange perversity would tempt an ancestor of the termites to turn quisling and undertake the difficult task of learning to live with their arch-enemies. Have you ever seen a cockroach in a skirt? Whether this means that myrmecologists should wear skirts or that Scots should become myrmecologists, I don't know; at least they would get no ants in their pants.

Despite the diversity of social habits in insects, there are a few features which appear common to all, and many of these are to be found in societies of other animals. These features in fact distinguish true societies from mere aggregations. The first of these is the subordination of the individual to the group, clearly necessary if grouping is to have survival value. This leads ere long to the inability of the individual to survive alone at all. Perhaps next in importance is the division of labour, leading to the development of different forms adapted to these different labours, and necessitating communication between them. As an offshoot of the subordination of the individual we have mutual feeding and stabilization of the food supply, and as the society begins to succeed and populations increase, a drift towards vegetarianism. Plant food or first-hand food is inherently more abundant and reliable than food on the hoof. Alongside of these developments we find the construction or adaptation of part of the environment as a home or nest and the control of conditions therein, especially temperature and humidity. And finally, perhaps as the price for all this security, perhaps as a displacement activity for the struggle for existence at the individual level, we have the development of intraspecific conflicts, of battles within the species. The intensity of socialization in any animal can be assessed from the degree of the development of these characteristics. We can try it on ourselves. And when we come to the final characteristic, wars and rumours of wars, we may remind ourselves of the myrmidons, ants changed into men, the bellicose followers of Achilles. Is this man's Achilles' heel?

If we look at current authoritative opinion on the origin of life and the course of its subsequent increase in complexity, this development of social units among animals seems a most natural thing. Characteristics which distinguish social units from the more complex solitary animals are often paralleled by those which distinguish complex solitary animals from the simpler ones that gave rise to them, and by those that distinguish each level of organization of matter from that simpler level immediately below it. The red blood cell of a vertebrate is involved in the mutual metabolism of the cells of its metazoan body, as the worker of honey bee, ant, or termite is involved in the mutual feeding of the rest of the colony. Like the worker insects, it has lost its ability to reproduce; neither can it survive alone. Communication between the cells of an animal is maintained by nerves and hormones, between the members of a society by senses and pheromones and mail and telegraph service, and between the atoms of a molecule to which they are subordinate, by electron bonds.

16

Populations, Pesticides, and Poisoners

HOW many insects are there? Not how many species, but how many individuals? Their numbers change faster than they can be counted so that no precise estimate is possible, but one of the best estimates made in recent years puts the figure at 10^{18}. A lot of insects. There are many closer estimates of numbers of particular kinds recorded. Springtails – the primitive soil dwelling insects which most people are not even aware of (p. 76) – occur in cultivated soil at densities around one thousand million per acre. A single swarm of locusts may weigh 20,000 tons, and since a locust weighs about two and a half grams this means about eight thousand million locusts. I have recently estimated the number of two species of ants, specialized ants living only in one species of tree in East Africa, at nearly ten million per acre. Despite their small size, when compared on a basis of weight of living matter per acre they are roughly equal to the ungulates on the Serengeti plains, one of the richest remaining game areas in the world.

On the basis of weight, let us look again at the total world population of insects, 10^{18}, but in doing so we should remember that the population of any one species may change by a thousand per cent in ten months. If we take the average weight of an insect as 2.5 milligrams, a conservative estimate, then the weight of living matter of the world's insects exceeds that of man by a factor of rather more than twelve. I think this factor is good and salutary, and we should be concerned if it falls much below this level.

Inherently numerous animals, insects have such tremendous powers of increase that it takes only a small change in their environment to occasion a large change in their numbers. If the change in numbers is upwards, we have a problem; a pest problem, for a pest is simply an organism that is too abundant (we have qualified for this title ourselves for a hundred years or more). Pest problems in insects have been alleviated for many centuries by the use of poisons, by chemical warfare. And although in public at least we condemn ourselves for it, the same pest problem in ourselves has also received this treatment.

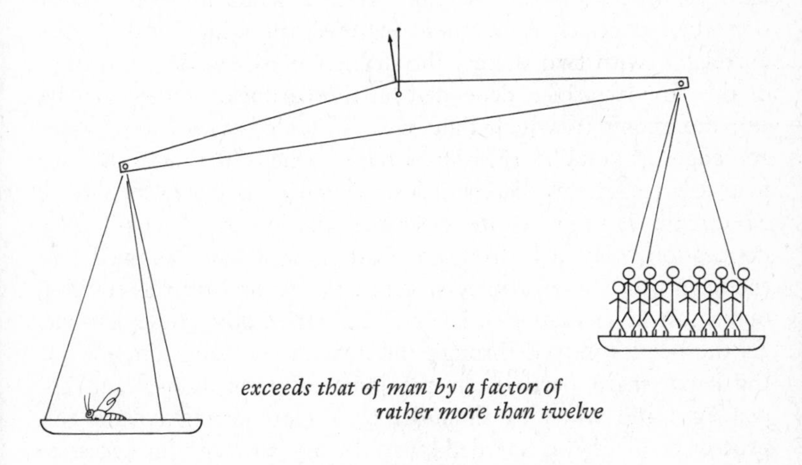

exceeds that of man by a factor of rather more than twelve

Of the many millions of people who use, profit from, or complain about insect poisons, few give a thought to how these act and very few devote serious study to them. It should be no surprise then that we still do not know how pyrethrum, the basis of flea powders of the ancients some 2000 years ago and still in use today, kills an insect. Indeed we are not yet always sure when an insect is dead. While pyrethrum is effective in a matter of seconds, DDT may take 24 hours to kill an insect. This should give us time to find out something of what is going on, but we certainly don't know the whole story yet for DDT either.

What then have we learned from the use of poisons? Strangely, perhaps as much about the physics as the chemistry of the insect. Some nice instruction in biophysics has been given by the inert dusts, so-called because they are chemically inactive. Materials of this type were used to protect grain in storage in the days of the pharaohs and have protected some of it to this day, but scientific investigation of them was delayed until the Second World War when other materials were unobtainable. Many preparations of similar nature – finely powdered, chemically inactive, stony or glassy materials – were studied with several kinds of insects, mostly beetles. After a while it became clear that the effectiveness of these materials in killing insects was correlated with two things: the dryness of the air and a quality of the powder which depended on the hardness of the particles and the extent to which they were provided with sharp points and edges; if you like, their abrasiveness. One of the most effective materials tested was diamond dust, which is hardly an economic insecticide. It soon became clear that the insects were killed by desiccation; they just dried up. And further work showed that the main protection of insects against this drying up was the thin outermost layer of the cuticle covering the body, the epicuticle. As the beetles moved through the dust or treated grain and got the hard, sharp particles in the joints of their bodies and appendages and worst of all under their close fitting collars, this protective layer was abraded away. In dry air, without access to water, death is quite rapid. Desiccation is a serious hazard to all very small terrestrial animals because of the high ratio of their surface area, on which the rate of water loss depends, to their tiny volumes, which dictate the amount of moisture they may contain (p. 21).

In the field of body chemistry the organophosphorus insecticides such as parathion and malathion, related to the nerve gases, have certainly taught us much even if we are not yet quite sure what. The old standby chemical for plant lice, nicotine, has long been known to poison vertebrates by interfering with the action of neurohormones, the chemical messengers which link up between the end of one nerve fibre and the beginning of the next, which cross the synapse, the gap between the branching terminations of adjoining nerve fibres. On these grounds, it was suggested many years ago that the mechanism of synaptic transmission in insects was similar to that of vertebrates.

The mechanism is this: the nerve impulse consists of an electrical change transmitted along the fibre; on reaching the end this electrical change occasions the release of a chemical, such as acetylcholine, which diffuses across the gap or synapse and is translated back into another electrical change on reaching the adjoining fibre. Its duty done, acetylcholine must be disposed of to restore sensitivity for a new impulse. An enzyme, acetylcholine-esterase, breaks it down. Testing the hypothesis that the same thing happens in insects has proved difficult and has only been accomplished in recent years. Insect nerves do indeed function in this way. The organophosphorus insecticides have helped to prove this, and proof has permitted new developments in this group of insecticides.

Organophosphorus insecticides appear to act by inhibiting the enzymes, such as acetylcholine-esterase, which break down the neurohormones. This means that impulses will continue to pass to the muscles in wild abandon, resulting in the symptoms characteristic of poisoning by these materials both in vertebrates and insects – tremors, convulsions, and finally death. It has been possible by using these poisons to work out the structures of the active centres of the enzymes, which is vital and valuable knowledge.

But more important than the similarity between synaptic transmission in vertebrates and insects are the differences which are now known to exist in transmission from nerve to muscle, neuromuscular transmission. These differences may permit poisons to be designed which kill insects without harming vertebrates. Organophosphorus compounds have also contributed to our knowledge of these differences, and here too neurohormones and enzymes play a part. We are beginning to reach the stage where these materials may be designed for particular purposes by juggling the five organic groups which may surround the pentavalent phosphorus atom in the insecticide. Our studies of poisons have also shown us that we have much to learn concerning the functions, chemical and physical, even of such seemingly simple animals as insects. We should be grateful for this knowledge as the first step toward remedying this deficiency.

Until we have done this, until we can design a poison for a specific insect, chemical warfare should be used against insects with cautions comparable to those we would like to see used before drugs are prescribed for our own use. Insecticides can be very valuable weapons, but they are weapons only and not a substitute for strategy and hard work. Wrongly used, these poisons will work against their own future usefulness as much as against the insects they are intended for; chemicals are dead and cannot evolve, while insects are alive and can. Without human aliveness in research to develop new materials, chemicals are very much at a disadvantage. This particular disadvantage can best be illustrated by a tale of long ago.

Mithridates the Great became King of Pontus in Asia Minor about 100 years before the birth of Christ. The epithet Great was appropriate only to his appetite, his physical size, and the number of murders he committed. This last point is the one which interests us, for Mithridates killed so many of his courtiers, relatives, and rivals that he had constantly to fear for his own life. Poisons were popular in those days, especially for royalty, and Mithridates is reputed to have protected himself against them by repeatedly taking small doses. In this way he so saturated himself with such old time favorites as arsenic that they no longer affected him. This proved his undoing, for when finally his sins caught up with him and he wished to kill himself, poisons proved of no avail and he had to hire the services of a Gallic soldier with a sword.

This piece of history serves to illustrate two points in connection with the poisoning of insects. Firstly, the amount of poison needed is, other things being equal, proportional to the animal's weight. Secondly, individual animals may acquire tolerance to poisons by the repeated administration of small doses. This effect is still known today as "mithridatism." A comparable

Mithridates . . . protected himself . . . by . . . taking small doses

effect in a population of insects lies at the root of the increasingly difficult problem of insect resistance to insecticides. How then does insecticide resistance develop? It has been described as the most convincing evidence for neo-Darwinian evolution, and indeed might have been foreseen once Darwin's theory was propounded. I cannot do better than expand this statement.

Animals of all species vary in a characteristic manner in respect of all their qualities. This variation is in part inborn, genetically determined; it is variation within a species, not between species (ch. 8). Most individuals show any particular quality in an average degree, while fewer and fewer of them have the quality in more and more extreme degree. Most of us, for example, are of average or near average height, while fewer and fewer of us will be found both tall and short. But in a large enough population there will always be the few individuals who are extremely tall or extremely short. Similarly in an insect species; most individuals will require an average or near average amount of a poison to kill them, but in a large population, and insects are not pests unless their populations *are* large, there will always be a few that will survive a very large dose.

So if we wish to breed a race of giants, the best procedure would be to liquidate everybody in the world who fails to attain a height of, say, six feet before reaching sexual maturity. Similarly, if we wish to breed flies resistant to DDT, the best procedure would be to kill all those flies which are more easily killed by DDT before they attain sexual maturity. This is just what we try to do. It has long been standard practice to recommend application rates of insecticides which kill most, but not all, of a pest population; and the selected survivors are the hardy ones. This practice is economic necessity because as the upper limit of 100 per cent mortality is approached, the extra dose needed to kill an extra insect becomes so great. Hazards arise for man, plants, and other animals. It is economic sense but, in the long view, biological nonsense.

By selectively killing houseflies more sensitive to DDT, man has bred, by unnatural selection, housefly strains which require to kill them 10,000 times the dosage of DDT required for their progenitors before the advent of this material. While the application of one tenth of a pound of DDT on an acre may be a practical, economic, and safe way of killing an insect, 1000 pounds per acre becomes impractical, uneconomic, and hazardous.

But we must add another fragment of history, for many people view insecticide resistance as a new problem. As long ago as 1908 a strain of the San José scale, a pest of citrus trees, was found to be resistant to lime sulphur in an area repeatedly sprayed with this chemical. One insect in six survived applications which previously gave good control. Scale insects, like houseflies, have a short life cycle; since resistance grows by steps in successive generations, this short life cycle favours its rapid development. Furthermore, female scales do not fly, so that individuals surviving from an insecticide cannot disperse and dilute their characteristics in an unexposed population.

There are four things about an insect then, which in the main determine the speed at which it will develop resistance to insecticides: its variation in susceptibility to the poison; the length of its life cycle; the proportion of its total population which is exposed to the poison; and, if this proportion is small, its mobility or flight range – the extent to which survivors mix up with unexposed individuals. Insects differ most in the last three respects.

With these features in mind, let us take a look at two familiar insect problems. First mosquitoes. Our northern species (p. 112) have a life cycle of usually one or two generations per year, long in comparison with many other insect pests. Vast populations develop across thousands of square miles of the arctic and subarctic, wherever snow-melt water for the larval stages is available. As yet chemical control measures have only been applied on a small scale in a few localities, affecting an insignificant proportion of the total mosquito population. Furthermore, these mosquitoes travel. Many species may be troublesome 20 or 30 miles (p. 43) from the nearest breeding areas. For their size they probably fly farther than most other insects. Thus it is unlikely that resistance to insecticides will develop rapidly in this group of mosquitoes. By contrast, some species of *Anopheles* mosquito which transmit malaria in the tropics may complete their life cycles in three weeks and thus complete a dozen or more generations in a year. Their populations may be large but are almost everywhere associated with man and they move in and out of his dwellings as often as he does himself. These dwellings are sprayed and these mosquitoes rarely fly more than half-a-mile. They are already so resistant that many insecticides are useless against them.

Bed-bugs might tell a similar story. The life cycle may be completed in a month, twelve generations a year; they are almost invariably associated with man, so that probably most of them sooner or later come up against his insecticides; and they have no wings so that any reserves of susceptible population which may exist are of little use to us. It is not surprising, then, that some bed-bugs are already resistant to more than one of our recently developed insecticides, and I fear we shall be hearing more about them if people will talk. But one of the biggest obstacles to their control is the resistance of people to talking about them. These rather graceless insects have one saving grace, they carry no disease.

These problems will become more intense and more urgent as human populations increase and the pressure on the environment both for places to live and places to grow food increases. What can we do about resistance? In a sense, we might as well ask what we can do about evolution. A return to the fly swat has been suggested, for surely a resistance to this weapon cannot develop. As far as the blow itself is concerned, perhaps not, but the ability to avoid it can certainly be increased by natural selection; indeed, resistance to poisons is sometimes of this behavioral kind. The useful life of poisons can certainly be increased if they can be developed in antagonistic pairs, so that resistance to one involves susceptibility to the other, and used alternately. But in the long run we should expect a strain resistant to both by a different mechanism to be selected out. Fortunately poisons are only one of many weapons in the armoury of the applied entomologist, one which has proved so valuable in recent years that alternatives have been neglected by comparison. Resistant insects force us to exploit these alternatives. House repair, for example, should play a part in bed-bug control; and since bed-bugs play an important role in the development of slums, perhaps we have a new and more urgent reason to consider this problem. And there is always biological control, in which the control agent is also alive and can also evolve to keep pace with the selection it exercises upon its host.

Nature is full of surprises. I find it intriguing to imagine the delighted surprise which Darwin might have felt at the unexpected direction from which comes, a century later, this telling support for his theories.

17

Bombs, Bugs, and the Future

WHEN I was discussing the title of this chapter with a friend of mine, he either mis-heard me, or at least made believe that he had done so. Bums, he said, should certainly be interested in the future of bugs, but are you sure that they will read this? There is much that needs saying on the topic of the relationship between bums and bugs, but that is for the future; it is bombs, not bums, that I am concerned with now; and should you have occasion to read this aloud, you might do well to spell it out.

Today one scarcely hears the word bomb in any other combination than A-bomb, unless it is the H for Hydrogen or C for Cobalt sub-species of this. While I do want to make some reference to this pretentious species of bomb, I have rather more to say about B-bombs and bug-bombs. Such old fashioned things as fire bombs, A.P. bombs, high and ordinary explosive bombs, and even doodlebugs and buzz-bombs are only on the fringes of my topic.

The word bomb has an onomatopoetic property. It represents an attempt to vocalize the sound which the thing itself makes; properly pronounced, it should sound like a bomb going off, a small one of course, and at a respectable distance. It is interesting to note here that the name bumble-bee or humble-bee has a similar property, so that my friend who mis-heard me was really doing nothing worse than mistaking a bumble-bee for an exploding bomb. And there is, incidentally, no etymological connection between a bum and bumble-bee.

Over the last few years an increasing number of domestic commodities, from paint to hair spray and from toothpaste to pie filling, has come on the market in pressurized containers having some superficial resemblances to bombs. On occasion, especially in their earlier days, these containers even behaved like bombs, distributing their contents in many undesirable directions at the least appropriate time. So perhaps it was all right, then, to call them bombs, as in the insecticidal variety, aerosol bombs, but this name has been dying as these devices have become more civilized. Some of us may live to regret the loss of this name, for even today's refined versions of these things behave precisely like bombs if consigned to the flames when their intended function is done. But now that the only sound they make in use is a re-assuring hiss they are often called dispensers – which has a horribly medical flavour for pie filling, although almost an onomatopoetic quality. One might almost call them hisspensers, except that the lady of the house might start looking for herspensers. They are also called aerosprays, which has that important modern sound, or just spray cans. I would like to suggest that we should go the whole hog for onomatopoeia and call them zizzicans.

Among the earliest successful pressure packs were several items of entomological significance, the best known of these being the aerosol bombs I have just mentioned. The name bomb, with its connotation of lethality, inspired confidence. Few people knew what an aerosol was so that this added the necessary mysterious touch. Aerosol bombs showed three attributes necessary for commercial success: effortless application, leading to extravagant use; ephemeral effect because the droplets disperse and leave little persistent deposit, so that they have to be used often; and an expensive and expendable container. That none of these is of technical value to insect control in the context in which they are used is, I suppose, neither here nor there, but that the first two, resulting in excessive use of insecticides, may contribute a hazard is a point I shall return to later.

You will also hear these zizzicans referred to as bug-bombs, but again surely bug-zizzicans would be more appropriate. The nice little anglo-saxon word bug originally meant an "apparition" or a "disgusting creature;" just how it came to be applied to such charming things as insects I can only guess. Entomologists have mitigated this misuse by restricting its application to one order alone, the Hemiptera, a group of winged insects with a simple life cycle and piercing and sucking mouthparts. One of the worst solecisms you can commit when talking to an entomologist is to refer to any other specific kind of insect as a bug. I have also heard zizzicans called bee-bombs, although it is difficult to imagine who would wish to use one against these insects. In any event, this name must surely be pre-empted for the closed skeps of bees which Greek naval tacticians catapulted onto the decks of the opposing vessels when battle was joined; real zizziskeps these, and appropriate forerunners of the buzz-bombs of the Second World War.

Successors to the twentieth century buzz-bombs, the doodle-bugs, are also of considerable entomological interest. Webster defines doodlebug as "any unscientific device with which it is claimed that minerals may be located." It is presumably in this sense that the name has been applied to ant-lions (p. 86), the ingenious larvae of neuropterous insects which are among the very few animals that have got the upper hand of ants. These sand dwelling insects use the flat tops of their heads as shovels to throw sand out in making themselves conical pits, at the base of which they lie concealed. The slopes of the pit have such an angle that they collapse underneath any insect that sets foot upon them. In this highly artificial environment, an enquiring mind is indeed a hazard; when ants are fatally curious about the rims of the pits, the ant-lions are lethally prepared with sickle-shaped jaws at the bottom. I do not know whether it is appropriate to describe the ant-lion as "an unscientific device," or whether, to fool the ants, it claims to be in search of minerals when digging its pit, but the name seems a good one. As for the doodlebugs of the Second World War, I am not sure whether this is a second-hand name derived from the resemblance between the craters they made and the pits of ant-lions, or whether, and I think more probably, it relates back to the original meaning and is a rather typical British wartime witticism commenting on the attributes of the adversaries as unscientific prospectors.

Passing on up the horror-scale of destructive weapons of war we come next to atomic bombs, and here I would like to start out by commenting on a news story of some years ago about some literally fabulous cockroaches which were supposedly breeding underneath the reactors at the Canadian atomic energy establishment at Chalk River. The newswheels of the world ground out this story for quite a time, so I thought I should find out about it. I asked a friend of mine who works at Chalk River and who knows roaches as they deserve to be known and he categorically denied that there were any roaches under the reactors. Enquiries in other quarters yielded the same result, and when I was there I had a look myself, also with the same result. Now this serves to illustrate two points, firstly, that you can't believe everything you read in the newspapers, nor in books, and secondly that somebody thought this story of the effects of radiation on roaches was sufficiently news-worthy to go to the trouble of making it up.

But even if there are no fabulous cockroaches underneath reactors, an atomic bomb will unquestionably kill an insect; it will kill it directly by heat and pressure, or it will kill it indirectly by atomic radiation. Most insects, however, can stand as much radiation as you and I, or more. Atomic radiation has been used in a number of ways to control insect populations; that it is not more widely used for this purpose is partially because similar doses are rather more likely to kill the operator. One of the first effects of radiation on insects is to cause sterility; this is the basis of what has come to be known as the sterile male technique for insect control. If the native male population of an insect, especially one which mates only once, can be swamped with an enormous artificially reared population of males sterilized by radiation, and if these compete for mates successfully with the fertile native males, most of the mated females will be infertile and the population will be reduced. This method embodies the sort of ingenuity that we are going to need more and more in dealing with insects, and it has had a great deal of publicity. But note the ifs. Its greatest test to date has been against the screw-worm fly which attacks cattle in the southern United States. The outcome of the test is still undecided.

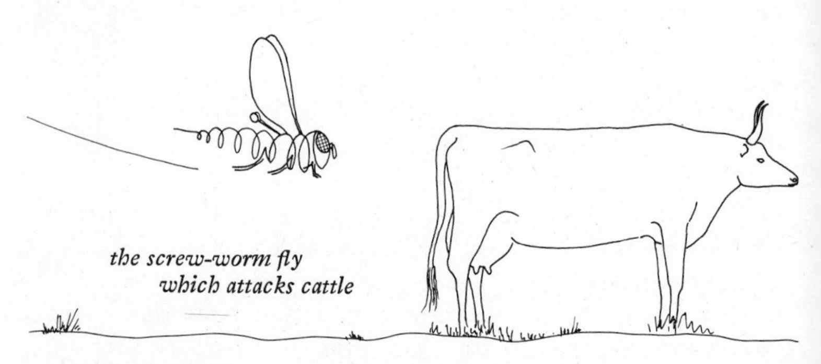
the screw-worm fly which attacks cattle

Another method which is under study is to attach fragments of radioactive material to laboratory reared males and females and release them into the natural environment, with the result that in addition to being sterile themselves, they will sterilize any of the opposite sex with which they may mate, instead of fertilizing them. In theory at least this would work better with an insect which mates many times than with an insect which only mates once. There are more of these insects, but less work has been done with the method.

Radioactive materials have also found wide application in studies of insects. They may be used in the field as a means of locating particular individuals and hence of securing information on their dispersal and behaviour, and they may be used in the laboratory in tracing the dispersal and behaviour of labelled chemicals, both nutrients and toxicants, within the body of the insect and hence give us a better understanding of its biochemistry. They can also be used to induce genetic changes in insects, and these changes may be valuable tools in helping us to understand evolutionary processes, in particular those processes which allow insects to develop resistance to our insecticides (ch. 16). Genetic changes may also be used directly in insect control.

Collectively these are powerful weapons for the control of insects, but some are also hazardous weapons for man; most people are now well aware of the dangers of accumulated radioactive materials in nature, whether from fall-out or any other source. The hazards from this cause are greater to man than to insects. I do not think we shall have radioactive zizzicans on the shelf at the corner drugstore in my lifetime, and I am glad.

Among the millions of insect species some stand ready to cope with almost any emergency, and all are adaptable; there is but one species of man, or some would have it, two. He is a die-hard conservative by comparison. Insects have great variability and a short life cycle; as a group they can adapt rapidly in many different directions at once and thus escape adversity or take advantage of opportunity. They have shown this time and time again in developing resistance to our insecticides. Man's long generations limit his rate of evolutionary change and he chooses more and more to control his environment instead of allowing it to control him. This is also a slow process and may sometimes prove irreversible, so that if mistakes are made, it may be impossible to correct them. His environment includes many other organisms, most of which are either essential to him or at least contribute in the long run to his well-being. In controlling his physical environment to suit himself, he must not lose sight of these other organisms nor of the interactions between them.

Make no mistake, if we put into our environment too much inappropriate poisonous or radioactive material, or bring about widespread changes in it before we fully understand the consequences these may engender, we may be among the first to go. Certainly we will precede many of the organisms we have been pleased to call our enemies, and neither physics and chemistry alone, nor technology will save us. Evolution will save the insects.

If bugs and bombs both have a bright future, we are unlikely to; or as Michael Flanders puts it:

The brontosaurus had a brain no bigger than a crisp,
The dodo had a stammer and the mammoth had a lithp,
The awk was just too awkward, now they're none of them alive
Each one, like man, had shown himself unfit to survive.
Their story points a moral, now its we who wear the pants
The extinction of these species holds a lesson for us – ants.

(Dead Ducks)

18

Centennials and Posterity

THREE hundred and thirty five years ago there was published at Popeshead Alley in London, England, a book called "Insectorum sive Minimorum Animalium Theatrum," written by one Thomas Moufet. Those were casual days, and Moufet also called himself both Moffat, and Muffet. Thomas Muffet had a daughter named Patience, and hearsay has it that she was the original little Miss Muffet now known in every nursery. At this distance in time nobody is likely to refute my statement that she was as beautiful as she was patient. I like to picture little Patience Muffet sitting on her tuffet at her father's feet as he worked on his book, and perhaps so distracting him with requests for more tales about woodlice or fireflies that finally, in desperate self-defense, he confronted her with the spider which had the effect described in the nursery rhyme. For if there is one thing more striking than another about Tom Moffat's book it is the fondness he expresses for spiders with their skin "so soft, smooth, polished and neat," and their "fingers that the most gallant Virgins desire to have theirs like them, long, slender, round, of exact feeling, that there is no man, nor any creature, that can compare with her." If I may say so, a most unusual fondness!

Twenty-four years later in 1658, in English translation under the title "The Theatre of Insects," Thomas Moffat's book was the first to be published on insects in English. These were some of the beginnings of the recorded study of these six-legged animals in armour, the beginnings of what we now call entomology. And four years after this publication, in Great Britain in 1662, the Royal Society, the oldest scientific society still operating, received its charter. It is interesting to note that in each succeeding century there have been important scientific and especially biological events at about this time, the late fifties or early sixties.

I like to picture little Patience Muffet

In 1758 Karl Linnaeus, the great Swedish collector of plants and other specimens published the tenth edition of his *Systema Naturae* in which he described in latin all the then known plants and animals and gave to each a pair of latin names, the greatest christening the world has ever known. His system of naming is followed to this day and the scientific naming of most plants and animals must be traced back to his work.

In 1859 Charles Darwin's "Origin of Species by means of Natural Selection" was published. There was an outcry, of course, from those who found the import of this carefully reasoned and long matured work hard to stomach. But when this had subsided, the broad outlines of the way in which living things, man and insects among them, have developed through the ages were no longer questioned by those intimate with them.

In the middle of the 19th century our population passed the billion mark, and food for a billion of our mouths as well as 10^{18} insect mouths had to be sought largely in the New World. Events in Canada over the last hundred years exemplify those in many developing countries. On September 26, 1862, three years after the publication of the "Origin of Species" and five years before the British North America Act, beards and butterfly nets were in evidence in the larval city of Toronto. An Anglican clergyman, the Reverend C. J. S. Bethune, a druggist, William Saunders, and a professor, Henry Croft, arranged a meeting for April of 1863 at which ten persons were present and at which the Entomological Society of Canada was brought into this world. This society in 1963 celebrated its hundredth birthday, its centennial, four years ahead of Canada herself.

The founders of entomological societies, with their beards and butterfly nets, were amateurs, bug-hunters; they studied insects because they loved to study them. This image of the entomologist dies hard, and so it should; collecting is an activity basic to the science of entomology. But do not forget that this is a science, in the sense that we have defined it (p. 5); a science fully as sophisticated as nuclear research and chemical synthesis and electron microscopy, all of which go with it. The entomological societies today include among their members experts in all these fields and their applications to the study of insects. What has occasioned this change from hobby to science?

There are now three and a half billion people on earth; three and a half times as many stomachs to fill; three and a half times as many backs to cover. The food and fibre needed have come in large part from previously unexploited lands in North America. Many thousands of square miles of prairie and forest, rolling hills and river valleys have been taken over by man and converted to farmsteads and woodlots and ranches to produce the necessary raw materials. In this process many billions of insects – hundreds of thousands of different kinds – have been confronted with changed circumstances favourable to some, fatal to others. With insects, as with man, favourable circumstances meant large families and population growth, so that human population growth has meant the concomitant growth of populations of some insects whose interests conflict with man's – who eat the same food or like the same environment. And fatal circumstances also affected insects helpful to man, so that we have not only the pest problems of wireworms, cutworms, and mosquitoes, but also a shortage of pollinating bees and parasites on the pests.

Added to these problems of population, our new human populations traveled further and faster and took with them, usually willy nilly, insects from elsewhere into new and bountiful habitats, leaving the enemies of them, parasites and predators and diseases, behind.

The Colorado beetle transferred from its rare natural food plant to pure crop potatoes and its population exploded. Cutworms and wireworms were given new areas of refuge below ground by the beneficent practice of ploughing and their populations exploded. The wheat stem sawfly transferred from native grasses into wheat – what else could it do? Its parasite pursuers were confused and its population exploded. The gypsy moth was brought over from Europe by accident, and in its new parasite-free habitat its population exploded to devastate broadleaved trees. In a new and growing country with small population and meagre resources, the farmers and the ranchers, the lumbermen and the trappers turned to their governments for aid, and the governments hadn't a clue. Who had a clue? None but the bug-hunters, the amateur bug-hunters, the beards and the butterfly nets.

These men were few in numbers; the original membership of

Canada's Entomological Society was only twenty-five. They had other jobs. And they had nothing against insects. But they solved many of these complex early problems in their spare time. Recognizing the necessity for insect control, they turned to in the true spirit of science and observed and toiled long hours objectively. They set aside their own interests to seek answers to problems which baffled the country. The governments, let's face it, exploited them shamefully, for they could do nought else. The Government of Ontario gave the infant society $400 a year for its services; rarely did a government get so much for its money.

James Fletcher, a distinguished naturalist, wrote to Canada's federal Minister of Agriculture on December 31st, 1884, in these words: "Sir, I have the honour to report that, in accordance with your instructions, I have, since my appointment as Entomologist to your department in June last been engaged in the investigation of the ravages committed by insects among the farm and garden crops and on fruit and forest trees." But we should note that his appointment was an honorary one, part time from his duties as an accountant in the Library of Parliament. The body of his report indicates that he really did do what he said; he investigated this wide range of problems. He was even able to check up on Ontario merchants supplying Paris green for poisoning the potato beetle: "Sample No. 5, a quarter pound packet cost 10 cents and contained 11.62 per cent impurity. I refrain from publishing the names of the vendors on this occasion, but would suggest that this be done next year unless they supply a better product to the agricultural community, whost interests you are protecting." His report concluded with a note: "small packets of insects sent for identification . . . can be sent postage free." In 1887 James Fletcher became full time Dominion Entomologist and Botanist (either position would be more than enough for most of us today), and from then on it was gradually recognized that the economic threats from insects called for economic provision to supplement the love of the amateur in the study of them.

In 1956 Canada was host to the tenth International Congress of Entomology in Montreal. Over 1400 people from 57 countries attended and 722 scientific papers were presented at one of the most successful of such gatherings held till that time. This Congress was organized and conducted by Canada's entomologists at short notice, to fill a gap in a series of congresses. These same men and women met in Ottawa in September, 1963 to celebrate and criticize the first hundred years' activities of their society and to plan how best to meet the challenge which will confront them in the next hundred years. Mostly it was to celebrate; could this be why history repeats itself?

South of the forty-ninth parallel those more competent than I could tell a tale of the last hundred years of entomology that would, in its outlines, be similar. Elsewhere, as men multiplied and entomology evolved from a hobby into a vocation, similar problems arose in the relationship between man, insects, and their common environment, differing perhaps in timing and intensity. Countries now developing and yet to develop need to consult with those that have experienced these problems. Can we take time to consider what we have to offer that they may do better? Is our attitude to insects and other animals the best one? Is it even acceptable? A consideration of these questions may help us to ensure that only the desirable things in history are repeated.

The interactions of insects with human history and culture are just a special case of a more general phenomenon, the interaction which occurs between all living organisms, plants and animals, to the ultimate advantage of the community. Probably only one organism has ever been able to flourish on this earth in isolation – the original "primeval slime," from which all life, perhaps, began. This interdependence of living things is one of the most striking facts that emerges from the study of ecology, the science of the relationships between plants and animals and their environment. Though some people would have it otherwise, man is no exception. Despite his television and wonder drugs, his atom bombs and space travel, man is just as dependent upon other organisms for his continued existence as any other member of the community of living things. And as yet he doesn't even know by name one half of these other beings upon which he depends.

Have we not been tampering a little too extensively with nature, in view of our ignorance? perhaps we are forced to it by our burgeoning numbers. Already in his short life on this planet man has extinguished more species than any other animal, and his cleverness does not yet extend to replacing them. The human effort going into biological discovery for its own sake is pathetically small in relation to that going into meddling with nature, call it eradication, agriculture, medicine, or what you will. Too often biological knowledge is insufficient for these applications and, as Goethe said, there is nothing more frightful than ignorance in action.

If the future of the world holds nothing else than more – many more – men and women, be they never so healthy and well fed, then it holds little indeed. Man needs a nobler objective than this; perhaps he may find it through the study of nature, through sparing a thought for other animals besides himself, for the rat in the rat-race.

We started this book with one animal scientist, the elephant's child, whose insatiable curiosity led him into perilous experiments with crocodiles and great uncles. We may bring it to a close by looking at some others. The mathematical abilities of animals are well documented; what of their scientific skills, their ability to extend their knowledge by hypothesis and experiment, by trial and error?

When the systematic position of man is examined on the basis of structure, he is clearly a close relative of the chimpanzee, the gorilla, and the orang-utan. Linnaeus placed man and the orang-utan in the same genus. Not liking this, otherwise eminent biologists have examined man's behaviour in an attempt to set him far more widely apart from other animals, selecting for this purpose language, the use of symbols, and activities in the realm of science. Now, while it is essential to use all knowledge about an animal in assessing its systematic position, nevertheless a balanced evaluation must be made. If man can really be set so widely apart from other animals on the grounds of his behaviour, we should indeed beware of drawing conclusions for him from experiments with rats. Psychologists have learned much from rats, though it is sometimes asked whether the psychologist trains his rats or the rats their psychologist. This is a frank admission of the scientific abilities of rats.

As we move further and further away from species related to us, leaving the birds and mammals and looking at reptiles, amphibia, and fish and then away into the invertebrates, molluscs and starfish, insects, worms, jellyfish, and finally the lowly amoebae and other protozoa, admittedly it becomes more and more difficult to recognize scientific activities. But we should be foolish to say that there are no scientists among these animals simply because our own techniques are not yet sufficiently sophisticated to recognize them. How many of us can discuss Avogadro's hypothesis with an avocet, or debate information theory with an inarticulate brachiopod? And yet some of us attempt to communicate with hypothetical extraterrestrial beings; would we not do better, as preparation for this if you will, to start at home? If our future should hold the keys to full communication with other species it might be exciting to look forward to.

We should here remind ourselves of Thomas Hobbes' dictum that: "There is no conception in man's mind, which hath not at first been begotten upon the organs of sense"; that all our knowledge, all our science, is at least coloured by our own sensory equipment. Could we communicate with other organisms we should be liberated from this restriction and free to use their viewpoints, their scientific ability, thus introducing a new dimension into biology – an introduction which would reverberate throughout the sciences. Much of the ground work for advances in this field has been done; information theory and computers will be invaluable. Bio-acoustics is developing, and we can now talk haltingly with porpoises; but sound is only one of many modes of communication, and we cannot expect them all to lie within our unaided ranges, or even within our methods of perception. Our rudimentary knowledge of the language of the hive bee has done great things for us. Will history record this, or the discovery of the structure of DNA, as the important biological event of the middle years of the twentieth century?

It can be demonstrated that most animals from the worms to man have scientific ability; we may say that this is probably true of some jellyfish, and possibly even of some protozoa. But to say that an animal has scientific ability is not to infer that it makes much use of it. It is a common error to fail to differentiate between capability and achievement; and even among men not all, fortunately, are scientists. In many simpler organisms one sees scientific progress largely as a function of a community or a colony or even of the species as a whole, rather than as a function of the individual. In similar vein our own most striking advances in science are becoming more and more dependent upon team work.

We see, thus, a kinship between scientific and evolutionary progress. Hypotheses which do not stand up to the test of perilous experiments in the environment become extinct and are known to us only as fossils in old books – but not to be ignored on this account. Surviving lines of plants and animals represent theories hopeful of life everlasting as facts, but in constant danger of extinction as fossilized hypotheses. Scientific laws are significant only in an environment, and not only are they all related but, like us and other organisms, interdependent. And so nature, and man as part of nature, uncovers by the experiments of natural selection the natural laws by which the current flora and fauna must live in the environment of today. This is surely the true meaning of cultural evolution. Our scientific ability is a product of evolution from the scientific abilities of other animals; it provides no grounds, nor have we other justification, for setting ourselves further apart than any lone survivor of a family. This is the essential message of Darwin.

A man's viewpoint as a biologist can be recognized by the manner in which he refers to his own species. Note, as a measure of man's rejection of Darwin's message, how often you hear the phrase "man and animals," and beware the remarks which follow. Only if a man consistently and unfalteringly says "man and *other* animals" can you assume that he speaks as one whose biological education measures up. Only when we all – psychologists, engineers, humanists, physical scientists, geologists, and, yes, even philosophers – speak, write, and think in this way will Darwin's work be done.

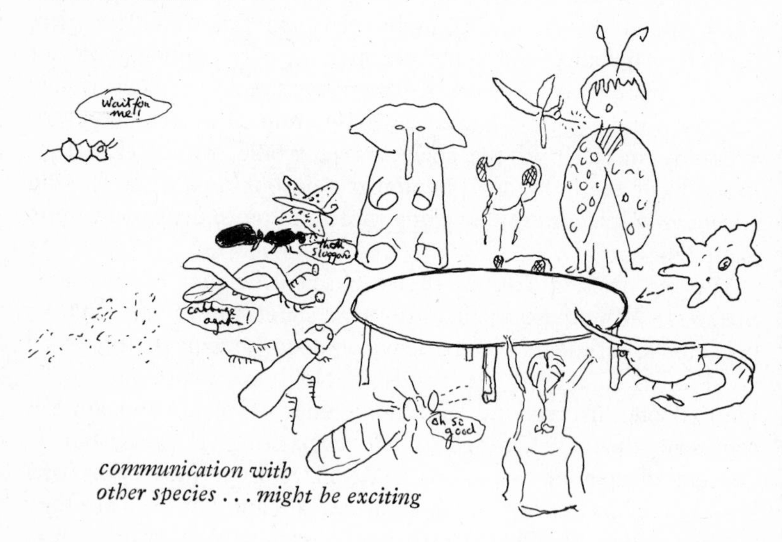

communication with other species . . . might be exciting

References

CHAPTER 1.

ARISTOTLE, Historia animalium. The works of Aristotle translated into English, (Vol. 4) by D'Arcy W. Thompson. Oxford University Press, Oxford, 1910. xv + "486–633" pp.

KIPLING, R., Just so stories for little children. Macmillan, London, 1923. 249 pp.

MONTESSORI, M., Il metodo della pedagogia scientifica. translation by A. E. George, The Montessori method, Stokes, New York, 1913. xlii + 377 pp.

MUYBRIDGE, E., Animals in motion. Dover Publications, New York, 1957. 74 pp. 183 plates.

PLEDGE, H. T., Science since 1500, A short history of mathematics, physics, chemistry, biology. His Majesty's Stationery Office, London, 1939. 357 pp.

CHAPTER 2.

CLOUDSLEY-THOMPSON, J. L., Spiders, scorpions, centipedes and mites; the ecology and natural history of woodlice, 'myriapods' and arachnids. Pergamon Press, London, 1958. xiv + 228 pp.

FARB, P., and the editors of Life, The insects. Time, New York, 1962. 192 pp.

LANHAM, U., The insects. Columbia University Press, New York and London, 1964. 292 pp.

PATTEN, W., Evolution of the vertebrates and their kin. Blakiston, Philadelphia, 1912. xvi + 486 pp.

WIGGLESWORTH, SIR VINCENT B., The life of insects. Weidenfeld and Nicolson, London, 1964. xii + 360 pp.

CHAPTER 3.

BRUST, R. A. and W. R. HORSFALL, Thermal stress and anomalous development of mosquitoes (Diptera: Culicidae). Canadian Journal of Zoology 43: 17–53. 1965.
DAVEY, K. G., Reproduction in the insects. Oliver & Boyd, Edinburgh and London, 1965. x + 96 pp.
HIGHNAM, K. C. (ed.), Insect reproduction. Royal Entomological Society of London, Symposium No. 2, London, 1964. 120 pp.
KALMUS, H., Variation and heredity. Routledge & Kegan Paul, London, 1957. xi + 227 pp.
ROSTAND, J., Bestiaire d'amour. Doubleday, New York, 1961. 128 pp.
WALKER, K., The physiology of sex and its social implications. Penguin Books, Harmondsworth, 1940. xi + 159 pp.

CHAPTER 4.

HOCKING, B., The intrinsic range and speed of flight of insects. Transactions of the Royal Entomological Society of London 104: 223–345. 6 plates, 1953.
LANGMUIR, I., The speed of the deer fly. Science n.s. 87: 233–234, 1938.
MAREY, E. J., Animal mechanism; a treatise on terrestrial and aerial locomotion. Henry S. King, London, 1874. xvi + 283 pp.
PRINGLE, J. W. S., Insect flight. Cambridge University Press, Cambridge, 1957. viii + 133 pp.
STILLSON, BLANCHE, Wings; insects – birds – men. Bobbs-Merrill, New York, 1954. 299 pp.
WILLIAMS, C. B., The migration of butterflies. Oliver & Boyd, Edinburg, 1930. 472 pp.

CHAPTER 5.

BUDDENBROCK, W. VON, The senses. University of Michigan Press, Ann Arbor, 1958. 167 pp.
DESCARTES, R., Discours de la méthode. Édition, de la Université de Manchester, 1941. xliii + 94 pp.
DETHIER, V. G., The physiology of insect senses. Methuen, London, 1963. ix + 266 pp.
HASKELL, P. T., Insect sounds. H. F. & G. Witherby, London, 1961. viii + 189 pp.

Myers, J. G., Insect singers, a natural history of the cicadas. Routledge, London, 1929. 304 pp.

Yapp, W. B. (ed.), The effects of pollution on living material. Symposia of the Institute of Biology No. 8, London, 1959. 154 pp.

Chapter 6.

Hocking, B., Smell in insects: A bibliography with abstracts. Defence Research Board, Ottawa, Canada, 1960. vi + 266 pp.

Moncrieff, R. W., The chemical senses. Wiley, New York, 1946. 424 pp.

Pettigrew, J. B., Animal locomotion or walking, swimming, and flying, with a dissertation on aeronautics. Appleton, New York, 1888. xvi + 264 pp.

Wilson, D. M., Insect walking. Annual Review of Entomology 11: 103–122, 1966.

Wright, R. H., The science of smell. George Allen and Unwin, London 1964. xii + 164 pp.

Chapter 7.

Broughton, W. B. (ed.), Colour and life. Symposia of the Institute of Biology No. 12, London, 1964. x + 146 pp.

Frisch, K. von, The dancing bees: an account of the life and senses of the honey bee. Methuen, London, 1953. xiv + 183 pp.

Hocking, B., Aspects of insect vision. Canadian Entomologist 96 (1–2): 320–334. 1964.

Savory, T. H., The world of small animals. University of London Press, London, 1955. 160 pp.

Sutton-Vane, S., The story of eyes. Viking Press, New York, 1958. 222 pp.

Urey, H. C., On the early chemical history of the earth and the origin of life. Proceedings of the National Academy of Sciences, Washington 38: 351–363. 1952.

Chapter 8.

Borror, D. J. and D. M. DeLong, An introduction to the study of insects. Rinehart, New York, 1954. x + 1030 pp.

Eddy, P. F., Insects in English poetry. Scientific Monthly 33: 53–77, 148–163. 1931.

IMMS, A. D., Outlines of entomology. Methuen, London, 1942. 224 pp.

TWINN, C. R., Insect life in the poetry and drama of England. Ph. D. Thesis, University of Ottawa, 1942. 281 pp.

WALTON, W. R., The entomology of English poetry. Proceedings of the Entomological Society of Washington 24: 159–203. 1922.

CHAPTER 9.

ARNETT, ROSS H., The beetles of the United States (a manual for identification). Catholic University of America Press, Washington, D.C., 1963. xi + 1112 pp.

HOCKING, B., *Hornia minutipennis* Riley: a new record and some notes on behaviour. (Coleoptera, Meloidae). Canadian Entomologist 81(3): 61–66. 1949.

MCELROY, W. D. and H. H. SELIGER, Biological luminescence. Scientific American 207: 76–90. December 1962.

REITTER, EWALD, Der Käfer: Ein Wunder der Schöpfung. Belser Verlag, Stuttgart, 1960. 206 pp. 60 plates.

RICHARDS, A. G. The integument of arthropods. University of Minnesota Press, Minneapolis, 1951. 411 pp.

TAYLOR, G., Some British beetles. Penguin, London, 1948. 55 pp. 24 plates.

CHAPTER 10.

FORD, E. B., Butterflies. The New Naturalist, Collins, London, 1945. xiv + 368 pp.

FORD, E. B., Moths. The New Naturalist, Collins, London, 1955. xix + 266 pp.

KLOTS, A. B., A field guide to the butterflies of North America, East of the Great Plains. Houghton Mifflin, Boston, Massachusetts, 1951. xvi + 349 pp. 40 plates.

PORTMANN, A., Animal camouflage. University of Michigan Press, Ann Arbor, 1959. 111 pp.

STEPHENSON, E. M. and C. STEWART, Animal camouflage. Adam and Charles Black, London, 1946. x + 195 pp.

WIGGLESWORTH, SIR VINCENT B., The physiology of insect metamorphosis. Cambridge University Press, Cambridge, 1954. viii + 152 pp.

CHAPTER 11.

BUXTON, P. A., The natural history of tse-tse flies: An account of the biology of the genus *Glossina*. Lewis, London, 1955. xvii + 816 pp.

CHRISTOPHERS, SIR S. RICKARD, *Aedes aegypti* (L.) the yellow fever mosquito. Cambridge University Press, Cambridge, 1960. xii + 739 pp.

CLEMENTS, A. N., The physiology of mosquitoes. Pergamon Press, London, 1963. ix + 393 pp.

CRISP, G., *Simulium* and onchocerciasis in the Northern territories of the Gold coast. Lewis, London, 1956. xvi + 171 pp.

HOCKING, B., Northern biting flies. Annual Review of Entomology 5: 135–152. 1960.

OLDROYD, H. The natural history of flies. Weidenfeld and Nicolson, London, 1964. xiv + 324 pp.

CHAPTER 12.

ATKINS, E. L., Mimicry between the drone fly *Eristalis tenax* (L.) and the honey bee *Apis mellifera* L., its significance in ancient mythology and present day thought. Annals of the Entomological Society of America 41: 387. 1948.

CLAUSEN, LUCY W., Insect fact and folklore. Macmillan, New York, 1961. xiv + 194. pp.

STRICKLAND, E. H., The ptilinal armature of flies (Diptera, Schizophora). Canadian Journal of Zoology 31: 263–299. 1953.

WEST, L. S., The housefly. Comstock, Ithaca, New York, 1951. xvi + 584 pp.

CHAPTER 13.

KINSEY, A. C., The gall wasps of the genus *Cynips*. Indiana University Studies, 16, Bloomington, Indiana, 1930. 577 pp.

LUBBOCK, SIR JOHN, Ants, bees and wasps: a record of observations on the habits of the social Hymenoptera. Paul, Trench, Trubner; London, 1929. xix + 377 pp., 6 plates.

MADDOX, H. A., Paper, its history, sources, and manufacture. Pitman, London, undated. viii + 159 pp.

MANI, M. S., Ecology of plant galls. Junk, The Hague, 1964, Monographiae Biologicae 12. xii + 434 pp.

WHEELER, W. M., The social insects, their origin and evolution. Paul, Trench, Trubner; London, 1928. xviii + 378 pp.

CHAPTER 14.

DARWIN, C., The effects of cross and self fertilization in the vegetable kingdom. Murray, London, 2nd ed., 1916. viii + 487 pp.

FREE, J. B. and C. G. BUTLER, Bumblebees. The New Naturalist. Collins, London, 1959. 208 pp.

HOCKING, B., Mead: a silk purse from a sow's ear. Canadian Bee Journal 63 (12): 4–6. 1955.

MACE, H., Bees, flowers and fruit: the story of insect-plant relations. Beekeeping Annual, Harlow, Essex, 1949. 184 pp.

PERCIVAL, MARY S., Floral biology. Pergamon Press, London, 1965. 243 pp.

RIBBANDS, C. R., The behaviour and social life of honey bees. Bee Research Association, London, 1953. 352 pp.

CHAPTER 15.

HARRIS, W. VICTOR, Termites – their recognition and control. Longmans, 1961. xii + 187 pp.

MICHENER, C. D. and M. H. MICHENER, American social insects. Van Nostrand, New York, 1951. 267 pp.

REAUMUR, RENE-ANTOINE FERCHAULT de, The natural history of ants. Alfred A. Knopf. Inc., 1926. xvii + 280 pp.

REED, LANGFORD, The complete limerick book. Jarrolds, London, 1925. 200 pp.

SKAIFE, S. H., Dwellers in darkness. Longmans Green and Co., London 1955. x + 134 pp.

WHEELER, W. M., The social insects. Kegan Paul, Trench, Trubner & Co., Ltd., London, 1928. xviii + 378 pp.

WILSON, EDWARD O., The origin and evolution of polymorphism in ants. The Quarterly Review of Biology 28(2): 136–156. 1953.

CHAPTER 16.

BROWN, A. W. A., Mechanisms of resistance against insecticides. Annual Review of Entomology 5: 301–326. 1960.

DEBACH, PAUL (ed.), Biological control of insect pests and weeds. Chapman and Hall, London, 1964. 844 pp.

HOYLE, G., Comparative physiology of the nervous control of muscular contraction. Cambridge University Press, Cambridge, 1957. 146 pp.

O'BRIEN, R. D., Mode of action of insecticides. Annual Review of Entomology 11: 369–402. 1966.

WIGGLESWORTH, SIR VINCENT B., Abrasion of the insect cuticle by aqueous suspensions of small particles. Nature, London 181: 779–780. 1958.

CHAPTER 17.

KNIPLING, E. F., The eradication of the screw-worm fly. Scientific American 203: October 1960. pp. 54–61.

O'BRIEN, R. D. and L. S. WOLFE, Radiation, radioactivity, and insects. Academic Press, New York and London, 1964. 211 pp.

WHEELER, W. M., Demons of the dust. Paul, Trench, Trubner; London, 1930. 378 pp.

CHAPTER 18.

BODENHEIMER, F. S., Materialien zur Geschichte der Entomologie bis Linné. Junk, Berlin, 1928 & 1929. Band I, 498 pp. Band II, 486 pp.

FRISCH, K. VON, Dialects in the language of the bees. Scientific American 207: 78–85. August, 1962.

KALMUS, H., Animals as mathematicians. Nature, London 202: 1156–1160. 1964.

KROGH, A., The language of the bees. Scientific American 179: 18–21. August, 1948.

LANYON, W. E and W. N. TAVOLGA (ed.), Animal sounds and communication. American Institute of Biological Sciences, Washington, D.C., 1960. xiii + 443 pp.

LINDAUER, M., Communication among social bees. Harvard University Press, Cambridge, Massachusetts, 1961. 143 pp.

MOUFET, T., Insectorum sive minimorum animalium theatrum. Thomas Cotes, London, 1634. 326 pp.

SPRAT, THO., The history of the Royal Society of London, for the improving of natural knowledge. Royal Society of London, 1667. 16 + 439 pp.

Index

Abdomen, 20, 104, 107, 133
Acetylcholine, 161
Achilles, 156
Acid, formic, 155
Acknowledgements, iv
Adam, 123
Advertising, 50, 51
(Aedes) excrucians (Walker), 113, 117
(Aedes) vexans (Meigen), 113
Aerosol bomb, 169
Africa, 116
Agassiz, Louis, 75
Aggression, 153
Alfalfa, 143
America, North, 114, 115, 125, 131, 138, 177
America, South, 108, 115
Ammonia, 93
Amphibia, 182
Ant(s), 149, 151-154, 170, 174
Antennae, 54, 60, 62, 66, 95, 97, 109, 142, 170
Ant-lion, 86, 170, 171
Anoplura, 82
Anther(s), 103, 143
Aphids, 13, 84, 85, 154
Appendages, 18, 22
Arabs, 132
Arachnids, 18, 19
Arctic, 117, 165
Aristophanes, 89
Aristotle, 9, 123, 185
Arnett, Ross H., 188
Arsenic, 162
Arthropods, 12, 15ff., 22, 23
Asia Minor, 162
Atkins, E. L., 189
Auricle, 143
Avogadro, 182
Awk, 174

Beelzebub, 124
Balsam gum, 117
Bamboo, 99
Bark, 134, 136
Bat, 36, 40, 49
Bedbugs, 75, 84, 110, 166
Bees, 29, 59, 90, 97, 120, 138ff., 170, 178
  bumble, 138
  hive, 71, 183
  honey, 145
  leaf-cutter, 138
Beetles, 13, 41, 58, 66, 85, 91ff., 160
  click, 96
  dung, 98
  oil, 96
  tiger, 92
Behaviour, 129, 172
Bethune, Rev. C.J.S., 177
Bible, 121
Bio-acoustics, 183
Biologist, 8, 27, 181, 184
Bites, 114, 115
Biting flies, 113, 115
Blackflies, 111, 114
Blood, insect, 16, 128
Blood, (warm), 110, 111, 113ff., 122
Blowflies, 98
Blunden, Edmund, 89
Bodenheimer, F. S., 191
Bombs,
  aerosol, 169
  atom, 168, 180
  bug, 168

buzz, 170
cobalt, 168
hydrogen, 168
Bombyx mori L., 106
Booklice, 81
Borror, D. J., and Delong, D. M., 187
Brontosaurus, 174
Broom, 143
Broughton, W. B. (ed.), 187
Brown, A. W. A., 190
Brust, R. A., and Horsfall, W. R., 186
Bryant, William Cullen, 83
Buddenbrock, W. von, 186
Buffalo gnats, 114
Bugs, 168, 170, 174
bed, 84
doodle, 86, 170
true, 3, 84
Bugonia myth, 121-123
Bull, 121, 122
Bulldogs, 115
Bumble bee(s), 39, 138, 143, 145, 168
Burns, Robert, 82
Butterfly, 13, 41, 50, 52, 58, 87, 101, 108, 123, 139
Vanessa, 108
Butyric acid, 93
Buxton, P. A., 189

Cabbage, 101, 104
California, 101
Canada, 115, 177
Cannibalism, 27, 29
Capsules, 150
Carbohydrates, 141
Carcass(es), 123, 129
Caribou, 117
Carrion fly, 129
Caste, 154
Caterpillar, 13, 58, 89, 101, 105-107
Cattle, 115
Cawein, Madison, 86
Cell(s), 70, 132, 156
germ cells, 28, 29
Cellulose, 151
Centipedes, 18, 19
Chalk River, 171
Chemical warfare, 159, 162
Chesterton, G. K., 63
Chilopoda, 19
Chinese, 95, 107, 131
Cholera, 128
Christophers, Sir S. Rickard, 189
Chromosomes, 29, 30
Chrysalis, 100, 105-107
Chrysopa, 86
Cicadas, 52, 84
Citrus, 161
Class, 75
Clausen, Lucy W., 189
Clay, 132, 135
Clements, A. N., 189
Click beetles, 96
Clothing, 118
Cloudsley-Thompson, J. L., 185
Clover, 145
Cocoon, 105, 107, 108
Cockroach(es), 150, 155, 171
Coleridge, Samuel Taylor, 88
Coleoptera, 85, 92
Collembola, 76
Colony, 154, 156
Colorado beetle, 178
Colouration, 106
Communication, 182
Corollas, 103, 104
Courtship, 29
Crabs, 18
Craster, Mrs. Richard, 57
Crisp, G., 189
Croft, Henry, 177
Crop, 145, 179
Crustacea(ns), 18, 19, 23
Cuticle, 160
Cutworms, 104, 178
Cynips, 134, 135, 136
C. gallae — tinctoriae, 136

Danube, 115
Darwin, Charles, 167, 176, 184, 190
Darwin, Erasmus, 85, 90
Davey, K. G., 186
DDT, 6, 128, 159, 164
DeBach, Paul (ed.), 190
Deerflies, 110, 115
De la Mare, Walter, 71
Dermaptera, 79
Dermatobia hominis (L.), 128
Descartes, René, 49, 186
Desiccation, 160
Dethier, V. G., 186
Dioscorides, 135
Diptera, 87

Disease(s), 121ff., 128, 166, 178
Dispensers, 169
Dispersal, 172
DNA, 183
Dodo, 174
Dogs, 117
Donne, John, 88
Doodlebugs, 168, 170
Douglas, Norman, 82
Dragonfly, 58, *65*, *66*, 77, 109
Drone fly, 123
Droppings, 126
Drugs, 180
Dung beetles, 98
Dunghill, 124, 125, 129
Dust, diamond, 160
Dust, insect, 160
Dynastes hercules L., 93

Ears, 50, 52, 53
Earwig(s), 80
Ecology, 180
Eddy, P. F., 187
Eggs, insect, 23, 30, 31, 58, 61, 83, 86, 94, 96, 97, 99, 104, 110, 112-116, 126, 128, 132, 134, 145, 150-154
Elephant's Child, 3, 6, 7, 8, 181
England, 132
Entomophobia, 14
Environment, 24, 28, 166, 170, 173, 178, 180, 183
Enzymes, 103, 104, 161
Ephemeroptera, 77
Epicuticle, 160
Eradication, 181
Ester(s), 141
Europe, 107, 125, 178
Evenus, 81
Evolution, 7, 8, 13, 23, 24, 28, 35, 70, 94, 125, 163, 166, 173, 184
Experiment, 4, 5, 181, 183
Eye(s), 49, 61, 64, *65*, 70, 111, 115, 116, 127, 142, 166

Farb, P., and editors of *Life*, 185
Fat(s), 41, 42, 104, 141
Fertilization, 29, 30, 32, 104, 144
Fever(s), typhoid, 128
Fibre(s), 131, 177
  fibres, silk, 107
  fibres, nerve, 160, 161
Fish, 115
  fish, flying, 36
Fission, 26
Flanders, Michael, 174
Flea(s), 83, 88, 89, 125
Fletcher, James, 179
Flies,
  black, 111, 114
  blow, 98
  deer, 111, 115
  drone, 123
  flower, 122
  fruit, 61
  hessian, 83
  horse, 111, 115
  house, 45, 125, 164
  hover, 122
  louse, 116, 117
  rangefinder, 67
  screw-worm, 172
  tse-tse, 116
Flight(s), 23, 34ff., 108, 164
Flower(s), 29, 139 et seq.
Fly (the), 8, 37, 52, 68, 97, 109, 164
Food, 156
Ford, E. B., 190
Formic acid, 93, 155
Fossil insects, 23
Free, J. B., and Butler, C. G., 190
Frisch, Karl von, 90, 187, 191
Fruit flies, 61
Fuel, 40, 42, 43, 108
Fungi, 154

Gall, 131 et seq.
Genitalia, 58
Germ cells, 28, 29
Glands, 105, 107
Glossina morsitans (Westwood), 116
Glowworm(s), 96
Goethe, 181
Grain, 160
Grasshoppers, 21, 52, 58, 64, 78, 84
Greek, 133, 170
Grubs, 94-99, 154
Gum, balsam, 117
Gut, 101
Gynandromorphs, 32
Gypsy moth, 178
Gyro-stabilizers, 109

Hair(s), 53, 138, 140, 143

Harris, W. Victor, 190
Haskell, P. T., 186
Hawk-moth, 53
Head(s), 170
Hemiptera, 84, 170
Hermaphroditus, 28
Hessian fly, 83
Highnam, K. C. (ed.), 186
Hobbes, Thomas, 49, 182
Hocking, B., 186-190
Honeybee, 32, 43, 44, 138ff.
Hood, Thomas, 80
Hornets, 121
Horseflies, 111, 115
Housefly, 125 et seq., 164
Hoverfly, 122
Hoyle, G., 191
Humidity, 156
Hunt, Leigh, 78
Huxley, Aldous, 84
Hybrid, 149
Hydrogen peroxide, 93
Hymenoptera, 89, 120, 153
Hypothesis, 4, 6

Ichneumon, 90
Imms, A. D., 188
Inchfawn, Fay, 80
India, 98, 107
Inert dust, 160
Infra-red, 69
Ink, 131 et seq.
Insecticides, 117, 119, 128, 160, 163, 164, 166, 169, 173
International Congress, 180
Iron, 134, 135
Isoptera, 81, 153

Japan, 107
Jaws, 92, 94, 143, 170
Johnston's organ, 53
Just so stories, 3

Kalmus, H., 186, 191
Khaki, 149, 150, 151
Kinsey, A. C., 191
Kipling, Rudyard, 3, 66, 185
Klots, A. B., 190
Knipling, E. F., 191
Krogh, A., 191

Ladybird(s), 97
Lamellae, 154
Landor, Walter Savage, 78
Lanham, U., 185
Langmuir, I., 186
Lanyon, W. E., and Tavolga, W. N. (ed.), 191
Lard, 117
Larva(e), 86, 95, 97, 111-116, 123, 126, 129, 154, 170
Latin, 135
Leg(s), 56 et seq., 94, 95, 105, 139, 143, 144
Lepidoptera, 86, 102, 103
Light, 66, 71
  infra-red, 69
  red, 69
  ultra-violet, 69, 70
Lilac, 125, 131
Lilith, 123, 128
Lime sulphur, 165
Lincoln, Abraham, 59
Lindauer, M., 191
Linnaeus, Carl, 121, 126, 176, 181
Lister, Martin, 135
Lobsters, 18
Locomotion, animal, 6, 23, 34ff.
Locust, 41, 44, 158
Louse (lice), 9, 13, 82, 83, 110, 116
Louse fly, 116
Louse, plant, 30, 160
Lubbock, Sir John, 53, 189

MacCrellish, Frederick, 6
McElroy, W. O., and Seliger, H. H., 188
Mace, H., 190
Maddox, H. A., 189
Maggot(s), 123, 126, 129
Magnolia, 131
Malathion, 160
Malaria, 113, 165
Malpighi, Marcello, 135
Mammals, 115, 182
Mammoth, 174
Mandible(s), 97, 102, 105, 116, 132, 143, 153
Mani, M. S., 189
Mantids, 58
Marey, E. J., 37, 186
Marquis, Don, 79, 83, 88
Marvell, Andrew, 90
Mating, 111

Maxilla(e), 102
Mayflies, 63, 66, 77
Mead, 146
Mecoptera, 125
Mediterranean, 134
Megalopolis, 151
Meganeura monyi (Brongniart), 45
Mendel, Gregor, 149
Mendelian ratios, 149, 150
Metabolism, 156
Metamerism, 16
Michener, Charles D., 192
Michener, M. H., 192
Midges, 113
Millipedes, 18, 19
Mimicry, 53, 106
Mites, 18
Mithridates the Great (VI Eupator), 162
Moncrieff, R. W., 187
Montessori, Maria, 4, 185
Mosquito, 31, 40, 58, 88, 102, 110ff., 128, 141, 142, 165
Moths, 83, 87, 101, 141, 142
- gypsy, 178
- hawk, 53
- yucca, 104

Moufet, Thomas, 175, 191
Moulting, 22, 23
Mouth(s), 110, 120, 177
Muffet, little Miss (Patience), 175
Mulberry, 107
Muscle(s), 35, 38, 43, 44, 109, 111, 116, 128, 160
Musca domestica L., 126
- *see* flies

Musket, 111
Muybridge, E., 185
Myers, J. G., 187
Myriapods, 18
Myrmecologist, 155

Nash, Ogden, 81, 116, 155
Nectar, 41, 42, 44, 51, 101, 103, 104, 110, 111, 114, 120, 141, 142, 145
Nerve, 160, 161
Nest, 133, 144, 154, 156
Neurohormones, 160, 161
Neuroptera, 86
New World, 50, 117
Nicotine, 160
Nose, 60, 62, 63
No-see-ums, 111, 113

Oak, 133, 134, 136
O'Brien, R. D., 191
Ocelli, 66
Odonata, 77
Odour(s), 60, 128
Oil beetles, 96
Oldroyd, H., 189
Old world, 117
Ophrys, 142
Orchid(s), 141, 142
Orders (of insects), 75, 85, 87
Origin of Species, 176
Orthoptera, 78
Ox, 121

Palps, 62
Paper, 132, 133
Papyrus, 132
Parasite(s), 112, 118, 178
Parathion, 160
Paris green, 179
Parthenogenesis, 30
Pasteur, Louis, 107
Patten, W., 185
Percival, Mary S., 190
Permafrost, 111
Pest, 159, 164, 165, 178
Pettigrew, J. B., 187
Pharaoh(s), 121, 126, 160
Phenolic compounds, 93
Pheromones, 155, 157
Phylum, 75
Picard, Malcolm, 25
Pigment(s), 151
Pledge, H. T., 185
Pliny (the elder), 65
Polarization, 71
Poison(s), 128, 159, 161, 162, 164, 166
Pollen, 51, 103, 104, 138, 142-144
Pollinia, 142
Population, 164, 165, 166, 171, 178
Porpoises, 183
Portmann, A., 188
Predator, 106, 107, 123, 151
Pringle, J. W. S., 186
Protein(s), 104, 110, 141, 151
Protozoa, 112, 115, 150, 151, 182
Psocoptera, 81
Psychologist(s), 182
Power (for flight), 41, 44

Pupa(e), 94, 112, 114, 127, 154
Pyrethrum, 159

Quoodle, 63

Radiation, 69, 171
Range-finder flies, 67
Rat(s), 181, 182
Ratios, Mendelian, 153, 154
Reaumur, Rene-Antoine Ferchault de, 60, 190
Red light, 69
Reed, Langford, 149, 190
References, iv, 187
Reitter, Ewald, 188
Repellent, 118
Reproduction, 26, 28, 29, 30
Reptiles, 35, 154, 182
Research, 5, 6, 7
Resistance, insecticide, 163 et seq., 173
Respiratory systems, 17, 21, 61
Ribbands, C. R., 190
Richards, A. G., 188
Riley, James Whitcomb, 85
Roaches, 79, 171
Rostand, J., 186
Royal Society, 176

Salmacis, 28
Salt, 105, 108
Samarkand, 132
Samson, 121
Saturnids, 102
Saunders, William, 177
Savory, T. H., 187
Sawflies, 89
  wheat stem, 178
Scale(s), 100 et seq.
Scale insect(s), 6, 154, 165
Scarabs, 98
Scoleciasis, 101
Scorpions, 17
Screw-worm fly, 172
Sea(s), 34, 70, 87, 105, 108
  sea water, 70
Secretion(s), 115, 132
Seed, 145
Segment(s), 18, 31, 109, 139, 143
Selection, natural, 8
Serendipity, 6
Serengeti, 158
Sex, 25, 35, 61, 64, 101, 134, 172
Shakespeare, William, 129, 135
Shapiro, Karl, 87
Shelley, P. B., 77
Ship, 108
Shrimps, 18
Silk, 101, 105, 107, 114
Silkworm, 107
Silverfish, 76, 102
Simulium damnosum (Theobald), 114
Siphonaptera, 88
Size, of insects, 20, 21, 23, 24, 35, 71, 83
Skaife, S. H., 190
Skeleton, 16, 35, 122
Sleeping sickness, 116
Slipstream, 42
Slug(s), 83, 96
Slums, 166
Smart, Christopher, 86, 88
Smell, sense of, 59 et seq.
Snails, 96, 116
Societies, 155
Soldiers, 152
Sounds, 52, 53
Spectrum, visual, 69
Speed, of flight, 43, 110
Spider, 13, 18, 19, 175
Spielman, Sir John, 132
Spiracles, 17
Sprat, Thomas, 191
Springtails, 76, 158
Stanford, Leland, 6
Stein, Dr. Sir Aurel, 132
Stephenson, E. M., and Stewart, C., 188
Sterility, 171
Stillson, Blanche, 186
Stomach, 145
Strickland, E. H., 189
Sturgeon, 115
Sugar(s), 103, 104, 108, 141
Sutton-Vane, S., 189
Swarm(s), 111, 112, 121-123
Swinburne, A. C., 88
Systema Naturae, 176

Taste, sense of, 60
Tar, 117
Taylor, G., 188
Temperature, 25ff., 30, 32, 156

Tennyson, Alfred, Lord, 77, 88
Termitarium, 152
Termites, 81, 149-155
"Theatre of Insects," 175
Theophrastus, 135
Thompson, D'Arcy W., 187
Thorax, 20, 24, 44, 53, 96, 109
Thrips, 83
Thysanoptera, 83
Thysanura, 76
Ticks, 18
Tiger beetle, 93
Toledo, 132
Tongue(s), 103, 116, 143
Toronto, 177
Trichoptera, 86
Trichopterygids, 93
Trihydroxybenzoic acid, 135
(Troctes) divinatorius (Müller), 82
Tse-tse fly, 116
Tundra, 111
Tunnels, 151
Turkestan, 132
Twinn, C. R., 188

Ultra-violet, 69
Ungulates, 158
United States, 172
Urey, H. C., 187

Vanessa, 108
Variation, 164
Vegetation, 114, 116, 126, 130
Vertebrates, 16, 24, 160, 161
Vespid, 137
Virgil, 122
Virus(es), 112
Vision, 64 et seq.
Visual spectrum, 69

Walker, K., 186
Wallace, Alfred Russell, 104
Walpole, Sir Hugh Seymour, 6
Walton, W. R., 188
War(s), 156
Warfare, chemical, 159, 161
Wasp(s), 89, 121, 122, 131, 133, 142
Webster, Noah, 170
Weevils, 91, 94, 99, 102
West, L. S., 189
Whatman, James, 133
Wheat steam sawfly, 178
Wheeler, William Morton, 190, 191
Wigglesworth, Sir Vincent B., 185, 188, 191
Williams, C. B., 186
Wilson, D. M., 187
Wilson, Edward O., 190
Wind tunnel, 42
Wing(s), 23, 34ff., 75, 81, 92, 102, 109, 117, 120, 151, 153, 154
Wood, 150
Worker(s), 153, 156
Wrigglers, 112
Wright, R. H., 187

Xenarchus, 84
Xyleborus fornicatus (Eichhoff), 94

Yapp, W. B. (ed.), 187
Yeasts, 62, 145

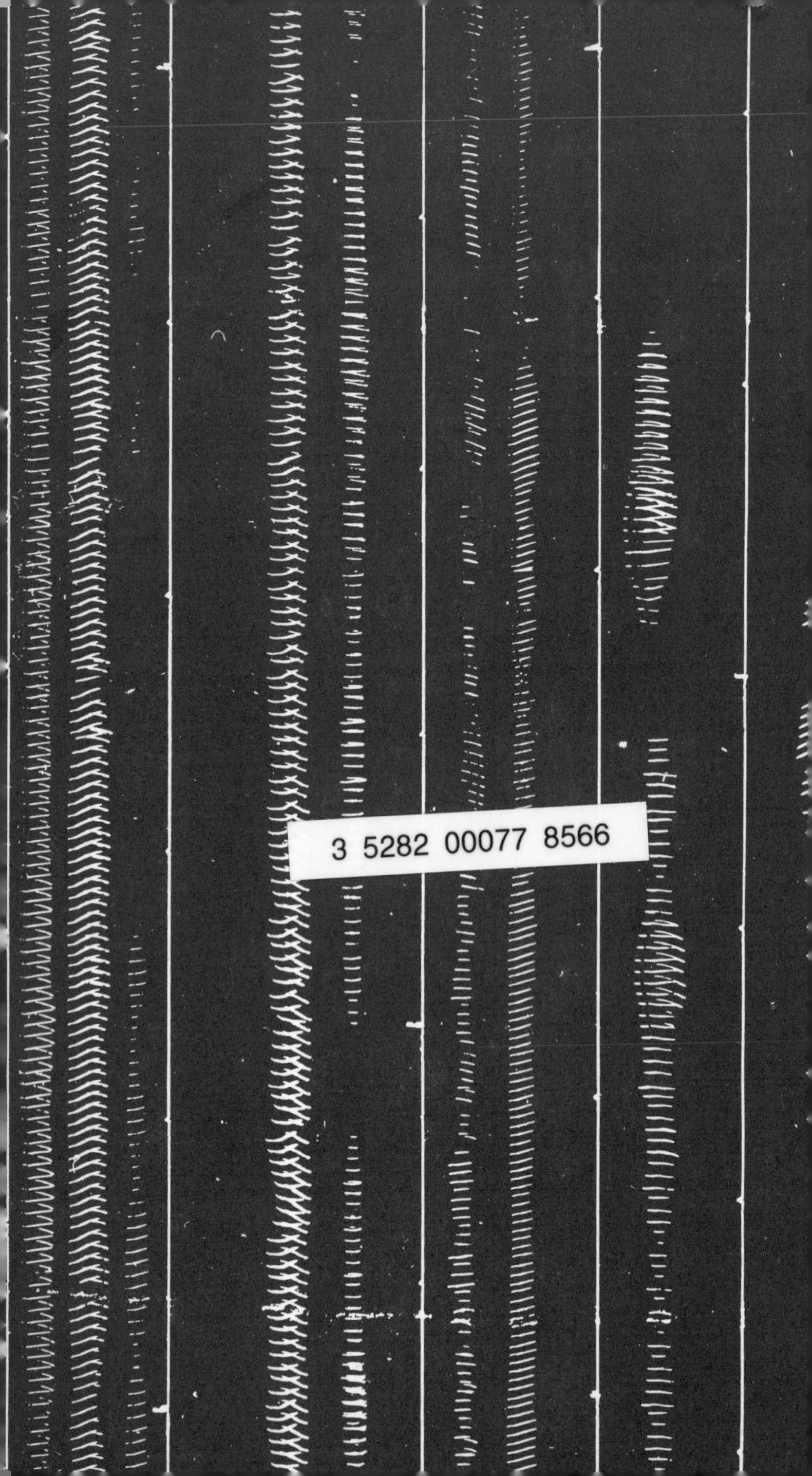